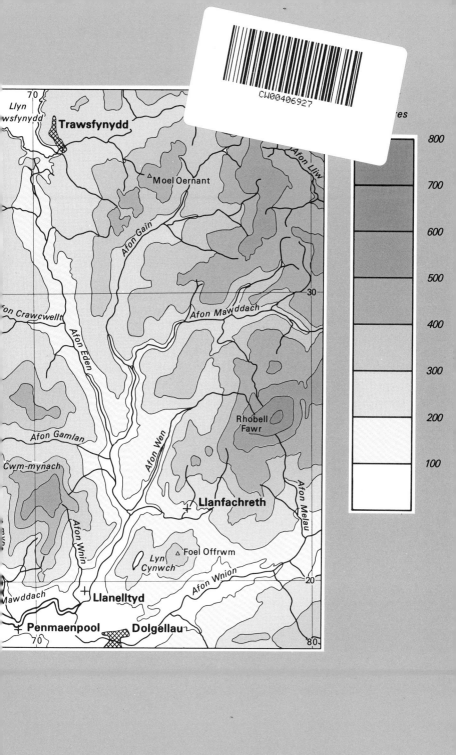

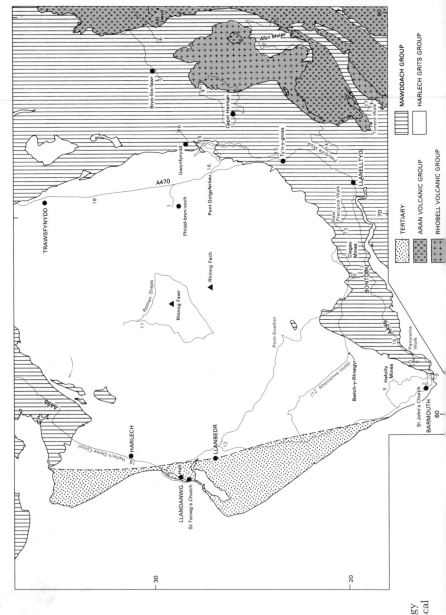

Figure 1 Simplified geology of the Harlech (135) geological sheet showing excursions

Classical areas of British geology

. M. Allen
udrey A. Jackson

Geological excursions in the Harlech Dome

1835 Geological Survey of Great Britain

150 Years of Service to the Nation

1985 British Geological Survey

BRITISH GEOLOGICAL SURVEY
Natural Environment Research Council

London   Her Majesty's Stationery Office   1985

Bibliographical reference

Allen, P. M., and Jackson, Audrey A.
1985. *Geological excursions in the Harlech dome.*
Classical areas of British geology, British
Geological Survey. (London: Her
Majesty's Stationery Office.)

Notes

National Grid references, given in the
form [7140 2863] throughout, all lie within
the 100-km square SH.

Numbers preceded by E refer to thin
sections in the collections of the British
Geological Survey.

Authors

P. M. ALLEN, BSc, PhD
British Geological Survey
Windsor Court, Windsor Terrace
Newcastle upon Tyne NE4 2HE

A. A. JACKSON, BA, PhD
British Geological Survey
Keyworth
Nottingham NG12 5GG

Her Majesty's Stationery Office

Government Bookshops
49 High Holborn, London WC1V 6HB
13a Castle Street, Edinburgh EH2 3AR
Princess Street, Manchester M60 8AS
Southey House, Wine Street, Bristol BS1 2BQ
258 Broad Street, Birmingham B1 2HE
IDB House, Chichester Street, Belfast BT1 4J*

*Government publications are also available through
booksellers*

British Geological Survey

Keyworth, Nottingham NG12 5GG

Murchison House, West Mains Road,
Edinburgh EH9 3LA

The full range of Survey publications is
available through the Sales Desks at Keyworth
and Murchison House. Selected items are
stocked by the Geological Museum Bookshop,
Exhibition Road, London SW7 2DE; all other
items may be obtained through the BGS
Information Point in the Geological Museum.
All the books are listed in HMSO's Sectional
List 45. Maps are listed in the BGS Map
Catalogue and Ordnance Survey's Trade
Catalogue. They can be bought from Ordnance
Survey Agents as well as from BGS.

*On 1 January 1984 the Institute of Geological Sciences
was renamed the British Geological Survey. It
continues to carry out the geological survey of Great
Britain and Northern Ireland (the latter as an agency
service for the government of Northern Ireland), and of
the surrounding continental shelf, as well as its basic
research projects. It also undertakes programmes of
British technical aid in geology in developing countries
as arranged by the Overseas Development
Administration.*

*The British Geological Survey is a component body of
the Natural Environment Research Council.*

Printed in England for Her Majesty's Stationery Office
Dd737396   C50   6/85

ISBN 0 11 884285 4

Preface

Contents

very year hundreds of students of geology visit the Harlech dome. The only guide to this classical area of Cambrian geology has hitherto been a geological map at one inch to one mile published by C. A. Matley and T. S. Wilson in 1946. To meet the needs of these visitors, this book which supplements the recently published 1:50 000 Harlech geological sheet, provides detailed geological notes and large-scale maps of carefully selected excursions in the Harlech dome. In addition, geological notes are provided (and a glossary of terms) for some of the more popular walks in the area, with the hope that they can be used by anyone with an interest in geology.

. M. Brown
Director

British Geological Survey
Keyworth
Nottingham NG12 5GG

January 1985

1 Introduction 1
Stratigraphy 1
Geological history 4
Geological structure 8
Mineralisation 9
Quaternary 9

2 Geological excursions 11
1 Ffridd-bryn-coch 11
2 Barmouth 13
3 Clogau goldmine 18
4 Capel Hermon 25
5 Bryn-llin-fawr 33
6 Allt Lŵyd 38
7 Upper Afon Melau valley 43
8 Llandanwg 47

3 Geological notes on popular walks 50
9 Barmouth to Hafotty mines 50
10 Panorama Walk 53
11 Roman Steps (Bwlch Tyddiad) 56
12 Drovers' Road, Llanbedr to Bontddu 59
13 New Precipice Walk 67
14 Precipice Walk 69
15 Ty'n-ygroes to Gwynfynydd 72
16 Pont Dolgefeiliau to Gwynfynydd 75
17 Torrent Walk 79

4 The Harlech dome road circuit 82

References 89

Glossary 91

Index 94

List of illustrations

1 Simplified geology of the Harlech (135) geological sheet showing excursion and foot path routes   ii

2 Generalised stratigraphy and tectonic evolution   2

3 Stratigraphy of the Cambrian and Precambrian   3

4 Turbidite facies model   5

5 Variations in stratigraphy of the Aran Volcanic Group   7

6 Stratigraphic range covered by excursions and walks   10

7 Geology of the Ffridd-bryn-coch area and excursion route No. 1   11

8 Geology of the Barmouth area and excursion route No. 2   14

9 Internal features of turbidites   15

10 Diagrammatic section of turbidite beds above the manganese ore-bed at St John's Church, Barmouth   16

11 Turbidite at the base of the Barmouth Formation showing complete 'Bouma cycle'   17

12 Solid geology and excursion route No. 3 around Clogau and St David's goldmines   19

13 Cambrian fossils   21

14 Contact of dolerite dyke against siltstone in the Gamlan Formation   23

15 Geology and excursion route No. 4 around Capel Hermon   26–27

16 *Lingulella davisii* (McCoy) from the Ffestiniog Flags Formation   29

17 Amphibole-bearing basalt   30

18 Paths to Llanfachreth over Cerniau and along Bwlch Goriwared   32

19 Solid geology and excursion route No. 5 at Bryn-llin-Fawr   35

20 Fossils from the Dolgellau Member   37

21 Geology and excursion route No. 6 in the Allt Lŵyd area   39

22 Sedimentary structures in the Allt Lŵyd Formation   41

23 Pillow lava   42

24 Geology and excursion route No. 7 in the Upper Afon Melau valley   45

25 Geology and excursion route No. 8 around Llandanwg   48

26 Geology of the footpath from Barmouth to Hafotty manganese mines (No. 9)   51

27 Panorama Walk, geology and footpath (No. 10)   54

28 Ice-scour gouge on Panorama Walk   56

29 Geology of Roman Steps and Rhinog Fawr (walk No. 11)   57

30 Geology of Llanbedr–Bontddu drovers' route (No. 12)   60–61

31 Pont Scethin   65

32 Burial chamber near Tal-y-bont   66

33 Geology of New Precipice Walk (No. 13)   67

34 Geology of Precipice Walk (No. 14)   70

35 Ffestiniog Flags Formation intruded by a thin sill of microtonalite   71

36 Ty'n-y-groes to Gwynfynydd (No. 15)   73

37 Pont Dolgefeiliau to Gwynfynydd (No. 16)   76

38 Geology of Torrent Walk (No. 17)   79

39 The Harlech dome circuit   83

40 Slumped sandstone bed in the Gamlan Formation   84

41 Fold in the Gamlan Formation   85

42 Basal Maentwrog Formation at Aber Amffra harbour   86

Introduction

1

Eighteen geological excursions and guides to popular walks are described in this book and, with the exception of some outcrops on the road traverse, all the localities described lie within the boundaries of the recently published Harlech (135) 1:50 000 Geological Sheet (Figure 1). Most of the area is in the Snowdonia National Park. Apart from the coastal strip from Talsarnau to Barmouth it is sparsely populated and used mainly for upland grazing and forestry. The principal topographical features, rising to heights of over 700 m, are the Rhinogs, which form an imposing spinal ridge, and Rhobell Fawr to the east.

Whilst every effort has been made to ensure that the routes are public rights of way, the footpaths may be changed from time to time. Ask permission from the land owners before leaving footpaths, refrain from climbing over dry stone walls and fences and always observe the Code of Conduct for Geology, published by the Geologists' Association. Special care should be taken at old mine workings some of which may be in a dangerous condition. You are strongly advised not to enter them.

Several people have helped us in the preparation of this book. Among them we should like to thank Ian F. Smith, Shirley Jackson and M. F. Howells for their help in the field and with the manuscript. Dr A. W. A. Rushton provided the palaeontological notes.

Stratigraphy

The exposed rocks in the area covered by this book are Cambrian and Ordovician in age. Rocks of Precambrian age have been encountered only in a borehole drilled through the lowermost Cambrian (Allen and Jackson, 1978) and are nowhere likely to be exposed. On the coast, however, under a cover of unconsolidated Pleistocene and Recent sediments, a thick succession of Tertiary, Jurassic and Triassic sediments was penetrated by the Mochras Borehole (Woodland, 1971). The complete sequence of rocks known in the area is illustrated in Figure 2.

Since the publication of the classic work on the area by Matley and Wilson (1946) this part of Western Merioneth has been called the Harlech dome. The 'dome' specifically refers to the structure of the Cambrian succession which is

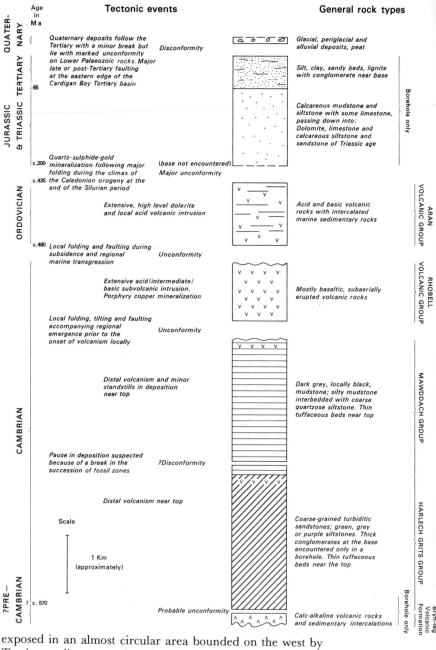

Figure 2
Generalised stratigraphy and tectonic evolution

exposed in an almost circular area bounded on the west by Tertiary sediments against the Mochras Fault and elsewhere by Ordovician rocks.

The Cambrian and Ordovician rocks are divided, in ascending order, into the Harlech Grits, Mawddach, Rhobell Volcanic and Aran Volcanic groups. This classification is used on the Harlech (135) Geological Sheet, and is the

Figure 3 Stratigraphy of the Cambrian and Pre-Cambrian

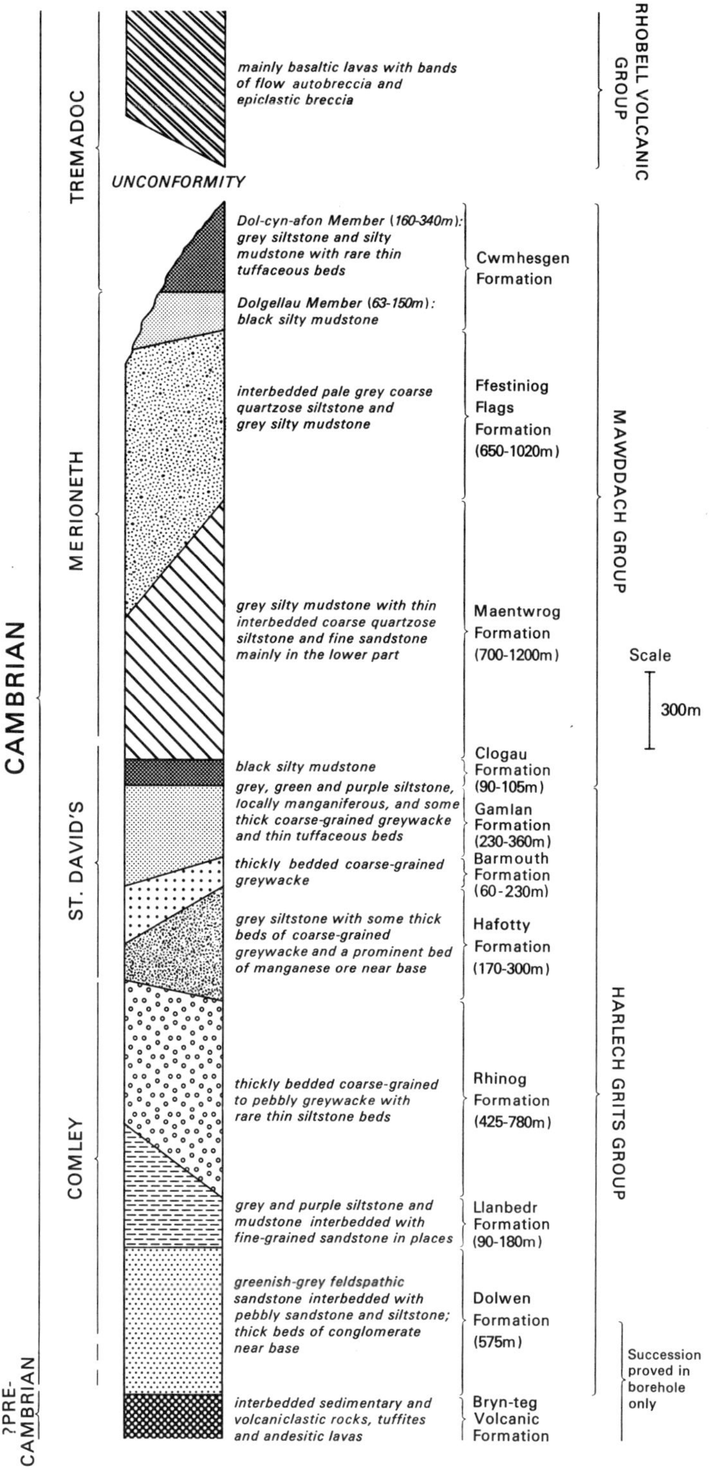

CAMBRIAN

RHOBELL VOLCANIC GROUP

TREMADOC — mainly basaltic lavas with bands of flow autobreccia and epiclastic breccia

UNCONFORMITY

MERIONETH

Dol-cyn-afon Member *(160-340m):* grey siltstone and silty mudstone with rare thin tuffaceous beds — Cwmhesgen Formation

Dolgellau Member *(63-150m):* black silty mudstone

interbedded pale grey coarse quartzose siltstone and grey silty mudstone — Ffestiniog Flags Formation *(650-1020m)*

grey silty mudstone with thin interbedded coarse quartzose siltstone and fine sandstone mainly in the lower part — Maentwrog Formation *(700-1200m)*

MAWDDACH GROUP

ST. DAVID'S

black silty mudstone — Clogau Formation *(90-105m)*

grey, green and purple siltstone, locally manganiferous, and some thick coarse-grained greywacke and thin tuffaceous beds — Gamlan Formation *(230-360m)*

thickly bedded coarse-grained greywacke — Barmouth Formation *(60-230m)*

grey siltstone with some thick beds of coarse-grained greywacke and a prominent bed of manganese ore near base — Hafotty Formation *(170-300m)*

COMLEY

thickly bedded coarse-grained to pebbly greywacke with rare thin siltstone beds — Rhinog Formation *(425-780m)*

grey and purple siltstone and mudstone interbedded with fine-grained sandstone in places — Llanbedr Formation *(90-180m)*

greenish-grey feldspathic sandstone interbedded with pebbly sandstone and siltstone; thick beds of conglomerate near base — Dolwen Formation *(575m)*

interbedded sedimentary and volcaniclastic rocks, tuffites and andesitic lavas — Bryn-teg Volcanic Formation

HARLECH GRITS GROUP

?PRE-CAMBRIAN

Scale

300m

Succession proved in borehole only

result of the progressive refinement of Sedgwick's (1852) original scheme by Lapworth (*in* Andrew, 1910), Wells (1925), Matley and Wilson (1946), Ridgway (1975), Kokelaar (1979), and Allen, Jackson and Rushton (1981).

The succession of Cambrian sedimentary rocks, some 5 km thick, is represented by the Harlech Grits and Mawddach groups which are divided into ten distinctive formations (Figure 3). On the south-eastern part of the Harlech dome the two uppermost formations of the Mawddach Group are overstepped by basaltic volcanic rocks of the Rhobell Volcanic Group. According to Kokelaar (1979) the group represents the remnants of a volcanic pile erupted during the late Tremadoc epoch and was originally at least 3.9 km thick.

Both the Mawddach and Rhobell Volcanic groups are unconformably overlain by about 1.2 km of volcanic and intercalated sedimentary rocks of Ordovician age named the Aran Volcanic Group by Ridgway (1975). The group crops out as a continuous belt of volcanic rocks around the southern, eastern and north-eastern sides of the Harlech dome. On the northern side of the dome Ordovician rocks younger than the Aran Volcanic Group are thrust over the Cambrian. The stratigraphical classification (Figure 5) of the group is based broadly on the divisions recognised by Fearnsides (1905) and Cox and Wells (1927). All formations except the Allt Lŵyd are defined by their volcanic character. The intercalated sedimentary units have not been named because of the difficulty of recognising them when the volcanic formations are missing.

Geological history

The oldest rocks known in the area are andesitic lavas and volcaniclastic sedimentary rocks of presumed late Precambrian age encountered only in the Bryn-teg Borehole (Allen and Jackson, 1978) beneath the Harlech Grits Group. The base of this group is also nowhere exposed but, in the borehole, about 40 m of conglomerate and pebbly sandstone appear to overlie the volcanic rocks unconformably and pass upwards into a deltaic succession, the upper parts of which are exposed at surface. These lower Cambrian rocks, attributed to the Dolwen Formation, mark the establishment of a sedimentary basin that covered all of Wales, much of England, parts of Ireland and extended into Belgium. The basin was situated on the edge of a continental mass which lay to the south-east, with the Iapetus ocean on the north-west.

Above the Dolwen Formation the Harlech Grits Group consists of grey, green or purple siltstone interbedded with thick units of coarse-grained, locally pebbly, sandstone of greywacke or quartz wacke composition that display the

Simple grading

characteristics of turbidites (Figure 4). Such rocks, derived from sediment deposited from turbidity flows, were first identified in this area by Ph.H. Kuenen, the pioneer Dutch sedimentologist. The discovery that coarse-grained sediment may be carried into deep sea basins by turbidity flows was one of the most important made in sedimentology this century. Two major invasions of turbidity flows into the

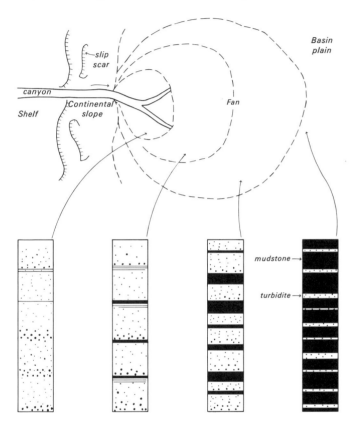

Figure 4 Turbidite facies model

Turbidites form in deep sea fans, many kilometres in diameter, at the mouths of canyons on the edge of the continential shelf. The sedimentological characteristics in a turbidite sequence change away from the source. The sediments near the canyon mouth are generally coarse and show little internal segregation. The sediments of the mid-fan show grading and internal segregation (intervals a to e, see Figure 9). Interbedded mudstones and siltstones are progressively more abundant towards the edge of the fan where base-absence sequences predominate (cde) and the sediments pass imperceptibly into the abyssal plain. Near the canyon mouth the inner fan is cut by major distributary channels, whereas the outer fan is mainly an area of accretion cut only by shallow channels not more than 1 to 2 m deep.

S. Dzulynski and E. K. Walton (1965) provide a comprehensive description of turbidites in 'Sedimentary features of flysch and greywackes'. Other sources are Ricci-Lucci (1975) and Walker (1965).

gradually subsiding basin are represented by the Rhinog and Barmouth formations (Figure 3). Palaeocurrent analysis for the Rhinog Formation (Crimes, 1970), indicates that current flow was from the north with a subsidiary easterly source, whereas in the Barmouth and Gamlan formations current flow was from the south or south-east. Both the Hafotty and Gamlan formations, which overlie the two turbidite formations, are manganiferous, and it has been suggested by Mohr (1964) and Glasby (1974) from geochemical studies of the manganese ore-bed at the base of the Hafotty Formation that these rocks were deposited in an enclosed, or partly enclosed, shallow marine basin. Such conditions, however, must have been short-lived and local. In the Gamlan Formation individual manganiferous beds rarely exceed a centimetre thick, and they are associated with thin tuffaceous beds which represent the first evidence of volcanism in the Cambrian of this area.

At the top of the Harlech Grits Group two major changes in sedimentary patterns are recorded; the Clogau Formation at the base of the overlying Mawddach Group (Allen, Jackson and Rushton, 1981) contains the lowest black, carbonaceous mudstone in the succession; locally, within the uppermost few metres of the underlying Gamlan Formation there is a marked change in the arenaceous component from coarse-grained sandstone, which is dominant in the Harlech Grits Group, to fine sandstone or coarse quartzose siltstone. The two predominant lithologies of the Mawddach Group are dark grey or black silty mudstone and white or grey coarse quartzose siltstone or fine sandstone. The latter rock type is rare in the Clogau Formation. The base of the overlying Maentwrog Formation is defined by the first appearance of fine-grained turbidites. A faunal hiatus at the top of the Clogau Formation suggests that there may have been a period of non-deposition at this time. Throughout the Maentwrog Formation, the turbidites, which diminish in abundance upwards, are closely associated with beds of coarse quartzose siltstone showing sedimentary characteristics similar to those in deep ocean contourites. Thus, though coarse material was periodically being introduced into the basin by turbidity flows, there was constant reworking of the material by sea bottom currents.

The basin became shallower during the later stages of deposition of the Maentwrog Formation, and the Ffestiniog Flag Formation was deposited largely in a shallow, tidal or alluvial/estuarine environment. The overlying Cwmhesgen Formation contains black carbonaceous mudstone, a rich fauna and thin tuffaceous beds. In it there are indications of several short pauses in deposition before the final uplift and emergence at the end of the Tremadoc. Although much of North Wales was emergent at this time, Lynas (1973) showed that locally in the Migneint, just north of this area, there was no break in sedimentation through the Tremadoc into the Arenig epoch. He attributed this to the strong influence of contemporaneous north–south block faulting on patterns of sedimentation.

At the end of the Tremadoc epoch the subaerial Rhobell Fawr volcano erupted in the south-eastern part of the area. According to Kokelaar (1979), eruption took place along north–south fissures marked by the complex of intersecting dykes on the west side of Rhobell Fawr. The preserved extrusive rocks related to this episode are predominantly basaltic in composition, but the co-magmatic

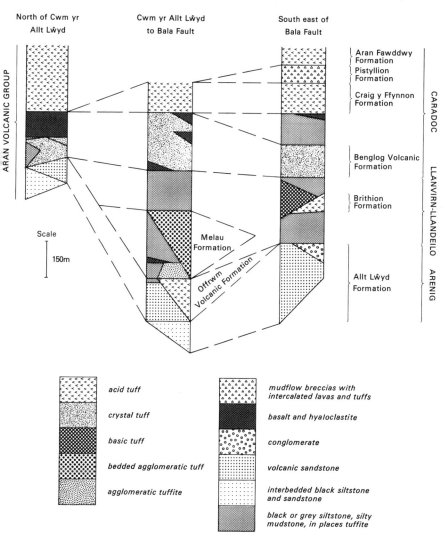

Figure 5 Variations in stratigraphy of the Aran Volcanic Group

intrusive rocks, which form numerous sills and laccoliths in the Cambrian on the east and south sides of the Harlech dome, include microtonalite and microdiorite in addition to the dolerite. A swarm of mainly NW-trending basic dykes which crosses the Cambrian rocks of the Harlech dome is possibly a product of this magmatic episode.

During the marine transgression at the beginning of the Ordovician period, the eroded and collapsed Rhobell Fawr volcano was submerged and clastic sediments were deposited in a shallow sea. These sediments comprise the basal part of the Aran Volcanic Group (Figure 5). They are overlain by epiclastic volcanic sediments, probably derived by reworking of contemporaneous volcanic rocks to the south and east, and they mark the renewal of volcanism during the Ordovician after only a short break. The overlying volcanic sequence includes rocks of acid, intermediate and basic composition, in deposits which consist of ash-flow tuffs, crystal-rich tuffs, agglomeratic mudflows, acid and basic lavas and hyaloclastites. Most of the volcanic formations thicken towards the south-east suggesting that the main eruptive centre was in this direction. The marked thickness variation of the Melau Formation, however, indicates a number of local and separate cones, each erupting basaltic tuff and lava into a shallow sea. The presence of intercalated siltstone throughout the Aran Volcanic Group suggests that the area was submerged, though there is evidence of some local emergence. Among the volcanic rocks, and apparently contemporaneous with them, are numerous dolerite sills.

Geological structure

All the lower Palaeozoic rocks in the area have been folded, faulted, locally cleaved, and regionally metamorphosed to low greenschist facies. The main structure of the Cambrian rocks is not a simple dome. It consists of the N-trending Dolwen pericline flanked on the west by two major parallel plunging synclines, the Caerdeon syncline which plunges south, and the faulted Moel Goedog syncline which plunges north (Figure 1). East of the pericline, though there are many large folds, the dip is predominantly eastwards. The structures are most likely the result of folding during the climax of the Caledonian orogeny at the end of the Silurian period (Figure 2), but recent mapping has identified local north–south folding both before and immediately after the Rhobell volcanism. Major faults, trending roughly northwards, were initiated in the late Cambrian, and continuing movement along them exercised some control on sedimentation. In the south-east of the area the NE-trending Bala Fault is the dominant structural feature. The N-trending Mochras Fault brings Tertiary sediments into juxtaposition with Lower Palaeozoic rocks in the coastal area.

Mineralisation

The Harlech dome has long been known as a mineral province. Ore deposits of four distinct types have been profitably mined in the area. About 44 000 tons of manganese ore were mined prior to 1928 from the bedded deposit of Cambrian age near the base of the Hafotty Formation. This sedimentary ore consists mainly of spessartine (manganese garnet), rhodochrosite and quartz.

In the area around Capel Hermon, Riofinex Ltd proved (but did not work) a low-grade, disseminated copper deposit of the porphyry type (Rice and Sharp, 1976). Subsequent work by Allen, Cooper, Fuge and Rea (1976) has shown that this mineralisation is genetically related to the late Tremadoc Rhobell Volcanic Group magmatism. A copper deposit at Glasdir, worked until 1914, is within a breccia pipe (Allen and Easterbrook, 1978) formed during this same mineralisation episode.

The Dolgellau gold-belt (Andrew, 1910) lies entirely within this area. A large number of quartz veins within it have been worked for copper, lead, zinc, silver and gold at least since the 18th century. Base metal production was never great, but two of the mines, Clogau and Gwynfynydd, produced about 120 000 oz gold. K/Ar age measurements on mica taken from these veins give a mean value of 405 ± 15 Ma (C. Rundle, personal communication), which dates the veins as end Silurian or early Devonian.

The youngest ore deposit worked in this area is at the Turf copper mine where peat, impregnated with copper minerals deposited from copper-rich waters draining the porphyry copper deposit at Capel Hermon, was dug in the early 19th century (Hall, 1975).

Quaternary

Superficial or drift deposits mask much of the solid geology in this area. Most of these deposits are the result of glacial or periglacial activity. At the climax of the last (late Devensian) glaciation about 17 000 years ago, the Merioneth ice cap, radiating from the Arenig to Rhobell Fawr axis (Foster, 1968), extended across the Rhinogs creating ice-scoured pavements in its passage. As the climate improved, the ice sheet gave way to valley glaciers which themselves eventually disappeared. The present-day landscape owes much to this period of intense glacial and periglacial erosion. The dominant features include U-shaped valleys, dry valleys, corries, rock basin and till-dammed lakes, as well as altiplanation terraces and stone stripes on the higher ground. Depositional features include drumlins and moraines, but there is a distinct paucity of fluvio-glacial gravels.

Along the coast, both the Traeth Bach and Mawddach estuary are drowned river valleys with thick accumulations

of alluvium. The intervening coast, however, shows signs of
accretion, with sand, silt, laminated clay and layers of peat
beneath the blown sand. Peat is extensive in upland areas
and along the coast, where marine erosion of the deposits, in
places, has left full sized tree trunks stranded on the shore.

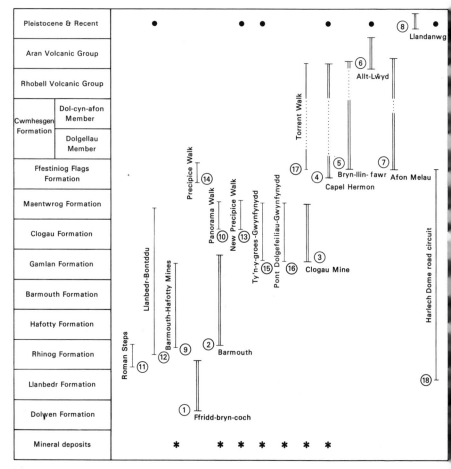

Figure 6 Stratigraphic range covered by excursions and walks

Geological excursions

2

Eight excursions are described (Figure 6), seven of which, taken together, cover the full Cambrian and Ordovician stratigraphic succession. The eighth is concerned entirely with Quaternary deposits. The stratigraphic excursions have been routed to show the principal characteristics of each formation, but details about structure, intrusions and Quaternary deposits are also included. In addition, three of the excursions include visits to the principal types of mineral deposit found in the Harlech dome.

The excursions are presented in stratigraphic order, but this is not necessarily the most convenient order in which to follow them. An estimate of the length of time that should be allowed for each is given. All eight excursions, which together form a good introduction to the local geology, can be undertaken within a week.

1 Ffridd-bryn-coch

On this short, fairly easy walk (about 1½ to 2 hours) on the eastern flank of the Dolwen pericline, the oldest Cambrian rocks in the Harlech dome, the Dolwen, Llanbedr and lower Rhinog formations, are visited. The localities (Figure 7) are numbered from east to west, descending through the generally eastward-dipping succession, but they may be visited in reverse order. Park in the lay-by [716 286] about 200 m S of Gelli-goch farm on the A470. Follow the minor road from the farm westwards over the Afon Eden to the bridge over the Afon Crawcwellt. Most of the exposures are in the

Figure 7 Geology of the Ffridd-bryn-coch area and excursion route No. 1

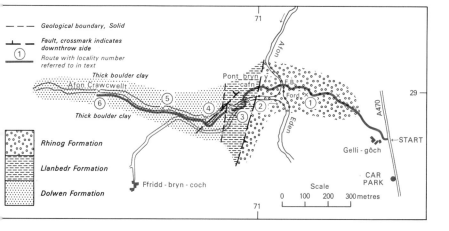

stream, and it is advisable to consult with the farmer at Ffridd-bryn-coch before visiting them.

Locality 1 A number of poor, small outcrops of coarse-grained, pebbly, graded quartzose sandstone are of the Rhinog Formation. The sandstone is typical of the Harlech Grits Group although it is better examined on the Barmouth excursion (No. 2).

Locality 2 On the east of the bridge and in the adjacent gorge are purplish grey and grey cleaved silty mudstones of the Llanbedr Formation. This is the lowest argillaceous formation in the Cambrian succession. It is exposed around the core of the Dolwen pericline and, to the west of the Rhinogs, in a belt south from Llanfair. Exact correlation between these two areas is difficult because of the presence in the west of interbedded sandstones in the upper part of the formation, which may equate to the lower parts of the Rhinog Formation elsewhere. A strong slaty cleavage is present in places, and locally this formation has been worked for slate. At this locality there are a few sills, as little as 0.5 m thick, of dolerite and feldspar-hornblende porphyry. They were emplaced about 3.5 to 4 km below the contemporary land surface during the Rhobell Volcanic Group magmatic episode in late Tremadoc times. The intrusions are displaced by a minor fault along the gorge, and they are gently folded.

Locality 3 The transition from the Dolwen to Llanbedr formations is clearly seen. Examined from west to east the predominantly green or grey interbedded siltstone and sandstone are overlain by 2 m of thinly interbedded pink and green banded and green sandstone and purple or grey silty mudstone with tuffaceous laminae. The sandy beds are less than 10 cm thick. The base of the Llanbedr Formation is taken where the purple silty mudstone is free of sandstone laminae.

The full thickness of the Dolwen Formation is some 575 m but the lower 280 m have been seen only in the Bryn-teg Borehole. The formation consists mainly of green or grey siltstone and sandstone, the latter dominant in three thick units in alternation with three dominantly siltstone units. There is an upward compositional change in the sandstone from lithic greywacke through subgreywacke to feldspathic greywacke and subarkose. In the exposed parts of the formation feldspathic greywacke is dominant with a few beds of coarse-grained subarkose. The sedimentary structures are consistent with the sediments having been deposited in shallow water, probably in deltaic or open shelf environment, under the influence of current or wave action. One fossil of Lower Cambrian age, *Platysolenites antiquissimus* was found in the Bryn-teg Borehole.

Locality 4 On the north side of the fault, there is excellent

lame structures

exposure of well bedded grey or green siltstone and commonly pyritic sandstone. The siltstone is alternately massive and
laminated. Locally there are thin beds of micaceous fine
sandstone, and 1 cm-thick magnetite-rich seams. The fine
sandstone beds show parallel- and cross-lamination, bands of
intensely convoluted lamination, flame structures and sand
balls.

Locality 5 The predominantly silty or impure fine sandy
nature of the Dolwen Formation is well demonstrated in this
section, but there is, in addition, an outcrop of coarse-
grained quartzose sandstone containing abundant detrital
magnetite. Such rocks occur only sporadically in the upper
part of the Dolwen Formation, though they are plentiful
higher in the Harlech Grits Group.

Locality 6 Thick deposits of locally derived boulder clay
have been progressively downcut by the Afon Crawcwellt
and there is evidence of an old stream course in about 60 cm
of cobbly sandy gravel with black manganiferous cement
resting on boulder clay about 2 m above the stream bed.

2 Barmouth

There are many excellent rock outcrops in and around Barmouth.
The bedding dips steeply east, and a traverse in this direction
crosses the full succession between the Rhinog and Maentwrog formations. This particular excursion, which follows a popular footpath from St John's Church to Panorama Hill and back into Barmouth along the coast road, is confined to the Harlech Grits Group.
However, it may be extended to include the Panorama Walk (p. 53)
along which there are good exposures of the lower part of the
Mawddach Group. Both this and the Panorama Walk can be ac-
complished in half a day. The route, in all about 3.5 km long and
rising from sea level to over 90 m OD, starts at St John's Church
[6128 1590], which overlooks the centre of the town (Figure 8).
There is only limited parking space near the church and it is advisable to use one of the car parks in the town.

Locality 1 The church stands on a platform cut into the
Hafotty Formation. Lithologies typical of the lowest part of
this formation are exposed in the rock-face behind the
church.

The lowest beds, exposed just above a bend in the road,
are pale grey parallel- and cross-laminated siltstone alternating with non-laminated darker grey siltstone. Several thin
resistant beds of pale grey pyritic fine-grained sandstone or
coarse siltstone stand out on the weathered surfaces. Some of
these show grading and load casts at the base. The siltstone
contains scattered lenses and nodules of manganese garnet
(spessartine), and the weathered surfaces show a
characteristic purplish brown patina with small pits where
the manganiferous nodules have weathered out. Higher up
the slope an overgrown adit has been cut into a quartz vein
which strikes at about 30° and is exposed in the hillside at

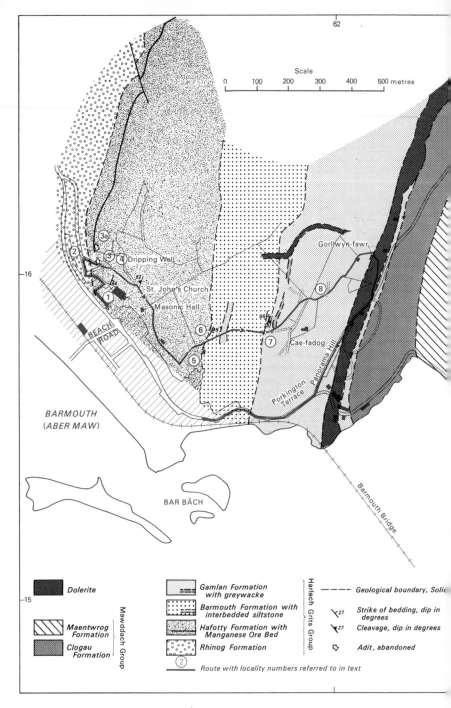

Figure 8 Geology of the Barmouth area and excursion route No. 2

'Dripping Well'. Beyond the adit a number of thick greywacke beds are exposed. They form the hanging wall of the manganese ore-bed, and persist for a considerable distance to the north. At St John's Church about four beds are exposed and they illustrate clearly the bedding features of coarse turbidites. The 'ideal' turbidite consists of five intervals (shown in Figure 9), and is collectively referred to as the 'Bouma-cycle'. The beds here show most of the intervals.

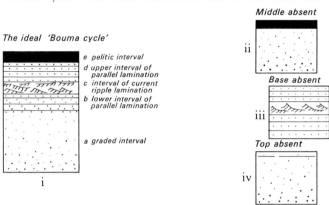

Figure 9 Internal features of turbidites

Superficially, turbidites may appear as a monotonous sequence of greenish grey greywackes beds but in detail there is much variation within individual beds. This has been described by a number of authors but is now often referred to as the 'Bouma-cycle'. The 'ideal' sequence (i) consists of five intervals labelled a, b, c, d, e. Numerous combinations of these are possible and some of the most common seen in the Harlech area are shown (ii to iv).

mple grading
ith large clasts at
p

They are up to about 60 cm thick (Figure 10), have sharp erosional bases, and show well-defined graded bedding from a coarse pebbly base to a finer-grained sandy top. Most of the beds have large fragments of siltstone incorporated near the top.

The greywacke beds are overlain by interbedded grey to greenish grey siltstone and mudstone and fine-grained sandstone with rare, fine- to medium-grained greywacke beds. The siltstone and mudstone are alternately evenly laminated, cross-laminated and massive. One 26 cm-thick greywacke bed shows all the turbidite intervals except the upper laminated one. The base of the bed, though sharp, displays large bulbous lobes and flames of the underlying sediment, caused by differential loading when the sediments were water saturated.

From here, return downhill to the bend in the road, and take a tarmac path which climbs steeply northwards up the hill. At the top of the hill the route follows the path leading off to the right. The next locality is at the junction of two paths. This is a good vantage point to view the Mawddach estuary, Fairbourne, built on a sand bar which reaches almost across the mouth of the river, and Pen y Garn, the westernmost peak of the Cader Idris range. Slate tips near Arthog across the estuary to the east mark the site of old quarries in the upper Cambrian slates.

Multiple grading

Locality 2   Here, coarse-grained greywacke of the Rhinog Formation, in beds up to 2.3 m thick, contains pebbles of quartz up to 8 mm long. Some beds show the full range of turbidite features described above (Figure 9). In addition, some of the thicker beds show multiple and reverse grading. The most common combination of bedding units here is *ae*.

Locality 3 [6125 1605]   A few metres to the north-east, the footpath passes back on to the Hafotty Formation, and a small trial pit marks the position of the ore-bed underlying the greywacke. Typically, the ore-bed is thinly laminated and superficially stained with a purplish brown residue from the weathering of the manganese minerals. It consists mainly of spessartine with some rhodochrosite, quartz, albite and chlorite (Woodland, 1939). Glasby (1974) suggested that it formed as a gel at the water/sediment interface in a shallow marine basin, initially as rhodochrosite, but was regionally metamorphosed to spessartine.

A short detour along the footpath to *Locality 3a* [6125 1609] shows one of the adits where the ore-bed was worked.

Locality 4 'Dripping Well'   This is an old adit into the quartz vein, first encountered at the church, which was exploited for copper and lead minerals. The adit is flooded and has been partially fronted with a low wall. The thick quartz

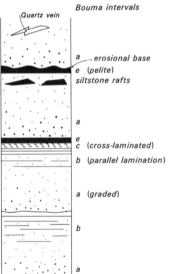

Figure 10   Diagrammatic section of turbidite beds above the manganese ore-bed at St John's Church, Barmouth

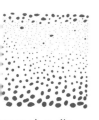

nverted grading
t tops of bed
grains have
migrated to area
f minimum
hear)

vein is exposed near the adit, but the adjacent siltstones are permeated with thinner veins.

Following the path to the SSE, there are numerous exposures in the Hafotty Formation. The path leads along the back of Barmouth. The siltstone is well cleaved near a bench [6154 1574] provided by the National Trust.

Locality 5 [6155 1577] Where the path passes through the wall, a number of thick, coarser-grained, quartz-veined greywacke beds near the top of the Hafotty Formation are exposed. Both *abe* and *ae* intervals are apparent. Through the gate the greywacke beds pass to the east into siltstone.

Locality 6 [6156 1569] At this exposure the argillaceous rocks of the Hafotty Formation are overlain by a thick unit of very coarse-grained, pebbly quartzose greywacke beds at the base of the Barmouth Formation. Several beds contain large clasts of siltstone, up to 15 cm long, near the top of the graded division. The lowest bed, 40 cm thick, shows the ideal 'Bouma cycle' (Figure 11). There is a well developed intersection lineation between cleavage and bedding on some bedding surfaces. The turbidites in this formation are similar to those in the Rhinog Formation and looking to the south-east, across a wall, they can be seen forming craggy knolls that contrast with the even surface of the softer weathering shales of the underlying Hafotty Formation on the hillside to the north-west. There is little intercalated mudstone or siltstone in this formation but, moving ENE to a hollow [6162 1598], there are some outcrops of banded siltstone and fine-grained sandstone similar to those of the Hafotty For-

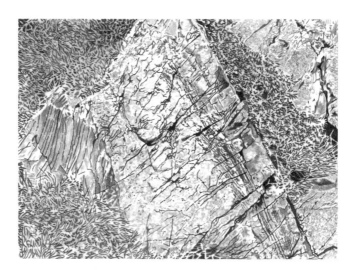

Figure 11   Sketch of turbidite at the base of the Barmouth Formation showing complete 'Bouma cycle'

mation. The turbidites in this general area show minor channelling at the base of some beds and multiple grading. In addition, a number of intercalated conglomeratic horizons occur with cobbles of quartzite up to 26 mm long. In places the conglomerate occurs as discrete beds about 5 cm thick; in others it is contained within the graded division.

Channel formed at base of turbidite bed by current erosion

Locality 7 [about 6174 1572]   The Barmouth Formation is overlain by thinly bedded siltstone, mudstone and fine-grained sandstone of the Gamlan Formation. The beds, 2 to 3 cm thick, are accentuated by parallel- and cross-lamination as well as colour banding. In this exposure the cross-lamination indicates derivation from the east. Also a 20 cm-thick bed shows asymmetric convolute-laminations.

Passing eastwards up the succession, some sparsely distributed beds of graded greywackes (1 to 9 cm thick, but rarely up to 1.10 m), interbedded with the siltstone, are exposed.

Locality 8 [6195 1595]   Opposite a five-barred gate leading downhill to Cae-Fadog, the upper part of the Gamlan Formation is exposed consisting of much finer-grained grey siltstones and purple-weathered mudstone. Careful inspection of this and adjacent exposures shows sparse, pale grey tuffaceous beds up to about 2 cm thick.

The path continues past Gorllwyn-Fach and joins the public road which leads back to Barmouth or to Panorama Hill.

3   Clogau goldmine

The mine is privately owned, but there are public footpaths around the mine area from which it is possible to examine the upper part of the Gamlan Formation, the Clogau and lower Maentwrog formations, some of the concordant intrusive rocks which characterise the southern side of the Harlech dome, some dykes, and part of the old workings. The route, about 2.6 km of easy walking, takes about 4 hours.

Access is by a minor road north from Bontddu Hall Hotel. Park near the telephone box at Pont Hirgwm [6677 1977]. The footpath, which is wide and well marked, starts by a cottage 240 m S of the parking place (Figure 12).

Near the start of this path is an excellent viewpoint: Diffwys, to the north, is capped by the Gamlan Formation with the Hafotty Formation on the east containing disused manganese workings. Cadar Idris lies to the south, and to the south-west the old Vigra gold mine is visible just above the boundary between the oak and coniferous forest.

Locality 1   The grey, altered intrusive rock is characteristic of the sills of microdiorite to microtonalite compositional range, which are common within the Cambrian rocks in this area. Such rocks, together with dolerite, are plentiful on the south and eastern parts of the Harlech dome.

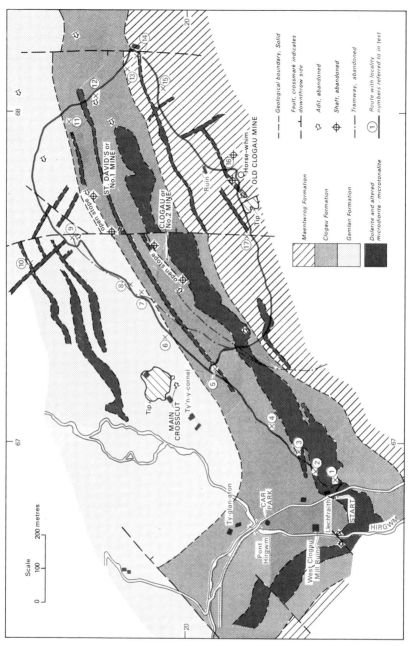

Figure 12
Solid geology
and excursion
route No. 3
around Clogau
and St David's
goldmines

Locality 2   The markedly discordant contact of an offshoot from the sill, seen at the previous locality, against baked grey silty mudstone of the Clogau Formation is well exposed. Despite the strong cleavage, which is nearly at right angles to it, the bedding is clearly visible in this outcrop. The strike is parallel to the NE-trending rocky features caused by the main intrusion on the hill above.

Locality 3   Another contact is seen to be concordant with the sedimentary bedding; the discordance of the previous locality is, therefore, probably only a local feature.

Locality 4   The Clogau Formation, about 95 m thick, consists of very dark grey or nearly black carbonaceous silty mudstone, commonly with lenses and laminae of pyrite or pyrrhotite with minor amounts of other sulphides. Sandstone laminae or beds, rarely more than 15 cm thick, are generally uncommon. In places the formation has yielded many middle Cambrian fossils, including the large trilobite *Paradoxides davidis* (Figure 13) which has been found near the Clogau mine.

Locality 5   An exposure in weathered, altered dolerite, probably forming a thin sill, shows an irregular upper contact against mudstone of the Clogau Formation.

Locality 6   The distinctive feature extending obliquely down the hill marks the top of the Gamlan Formation. Typically, this formation consists predominantly of green, grey or purple siltstone, but beds of coarse-grained greywacke-type sandstone occur throughout. In this area the first appearance of laminae and thin beds of quartzose fine sandstone of the type characteristic of the overlying Mawddach Group takes place within the upper part of the Gamlan Formation.

Below this locality is Ty'n-y-cornel cottage, and near it is the main adit of the Clogau gold mine driven in 1880–1884. Birch trees near the cottage are growing on the waste tips. More spoil heaps from other adits are present behind the wall to the south-east of this locality. About 45 m to the north-east the path crosses one of the old tramways.

Locality 7   Beds of laminated, quartzose fine sandstone, up to 3 cm thick, and similar to those in the lowest Maentwrog Formation, are present near the top part of the Gamlan Formation. Some show irregular bases, infilled eroded troughs and flat tops; other are lens-shaped.

Locality 8   A thin sill of altered dolerite, too small to be shown on the map, is seen here. Such intrusions diminish in abundance below the Clogau Formation. Beyond this locality, towards the north-east, the path passes progressively downwards through the Gamlan Formation.

In the crags along the path are beds up to 20 cm thick mostly of greenish grey greywacke. This rock is more abun-

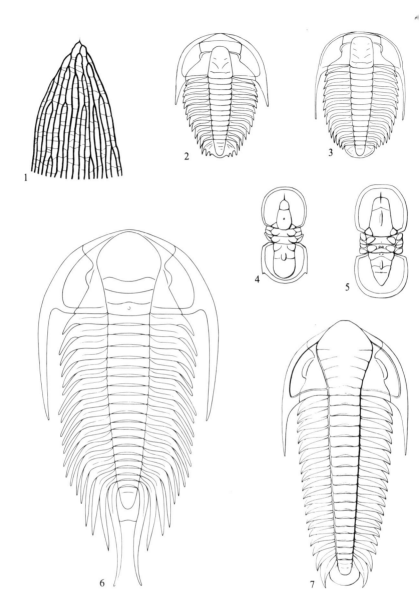

Figure 13 Cambrian fossils
1 *Dictyonema flabelliforme* (Eichwald), × 1, from the base of the Dol-cyn-afon Member of the Cwmhesgen Formation (Tremadoc Series).
2 *Parabolinoides bucephalus* (Belt), × 1, from the top of the Ffestiniog Flags Formation (Merioneth Series). 3 *Olenus micrurus* Salter, × 1, from the Maentwrog Formation (Merioneth Series). 4 *Homagnostus obesus* (Belt), × 4, from the Maentwrog Formation. 5 *Tomagnostus fissus* (Linnarsson), × 4, from the Clogau Formation (St David's Series). 6 *Paradoxides davidis* Salter, × ¹/₃, from the Clogau Formation. 7 *Paradoxides hicksii* Salter, × 1, from the basal Clogau and top of the Gamlan formations.

dant here than in the overlying strata. This locality is the lowest at which beds of fine quartzose sandstone have been found.

Locality 9   The well-made track ends at a tip outside one of the many adits associated with the St David's mine. The workings in the St David's mine are on the east of the Bryntirion Fault in the same vein system as that worked in the Clogau mine, west of the fault. The mines yielded over 80 000 oz of gold between about 1860 and 1911, with peak production in the years 1899–1907 (Hall, 1975). This work resulted in the excavation of over 15 miles of tunnels under the mountain. The open workings and stopes can be examined along the top of the hill, and there are many adits, shafts, and tramways. The old miners believed that gold-bearing parts of quartz vein occurred where the vein crossed the junction between a sill and the Clogau Formation — a coincidence which occurs at this mine. Little gold has been won from veins cutting formations below the Clogau. In the veins of the Dolgellau gold-belt, gold occurs in association with two main suites of sulphides. One suite is dominated by sphalerite, galena, and pyrite with rare chalcopyrite. The other, which includes the vein in this mine, contains pyrite, pyrrhotite and chalcopyrite with minor or rare galena and sphalerite. All these minerals can be found on the tip at this locality. The main gangue mineral is quartz, but an examination of the tip will yield much calcite, some chlorite, sericite and large included fragments of wallrock. The Clogau mine re-opened in 1980.

Locality 10   On the north side of the wall at *Locality 9*, two dolerite dykes 2 to 3 m thick can be traced north-west, cutting rocks of the Gamlan Formation. The northern dyke can be followed for about 150 m to a craggy outcrop, *Locality 10*, under two rowan trees. Here, at the contact, the bedding in the adjacent sedimentary rocks is sharply upturned (Figure 14). Also here, the dyke crosses a thin dolerite sill. In this well-exposed area, the graded beds of coarse-grained greywacke which characterise the Harlech Grits Group are common.

Immediately east of *Locality 9* the footpath, which is a few metres north of the wall, crosses the Bryntirion Fault. Along the footpath there are some excellent exposures of the Gamlan Formation, including a purplish grey siltstone which locally characterises the top of the formation.

Locality 11   The top of the Gamlan Formation is not exposed, but it coincides with a hollow or topographic slack. On the south of the slack, 3 m of dark grey mudstone of the Clogau Formation underlie a grey microtonalite sill. The view north from this locality is informative: the bedding on Diffwys can be seen clearly dipping westwards, whereas on Y

Figure 14 Sketch of contact of dolerite dyke against siltstone in the Gamlan Formation

Garn, to the east of Cwm-mynach, and across the axis of the Dolwen pericline, the bedding dips eastwards.

Locality 12 There are several thin microdiorite and dolerite sills here, and a short trial has been excavated in a quartz vein along the upper contact of one of them.

Locality 13 The Maentwrog Formation overlies the Clogau Formation with apparent conformity, but the absence of an important fossil zone at this level suggests that there may be a depositional break between them. The Maentwrog Formation consists of medium and dark grey mudstone and silty mudstone interbedded in places with laminae and beds (usually less than 40 cm thick) of fine quartzose sandstone or coarse siltstone. In this area the arenaceous beds occur only in the lower half of the formation, which led Matley and Wilson (1946) to divide it into a lower, Vigra, member and an upper, Penrhos, member. This distinction, however, is not apparent everywhere around the Harlech dome, and it has not been made on the Harlech (135) Geological Sheet. The basal part of the Maentwrog Formation is exposed here, folded about a roughly N-trending axis in a craggy outcrop with an oak tree on it.

The sandstones in this formation show two sets of sedimentary structures indicative respectively of deposition by turbidity currents and of reworking. The turbidites are locally graded, but are more commonly massive in the lower part of the bed reflecting the uniform grain size of the source material. Rarely, a layer of coarse grains can be seen at the base. Above the massive or graded interval is a parallel-laminated interval (*ab* – see Figure 9) or simply the uppermost pelitic interval (*ae*). Commonly the beds show complex convolute-lamination, possibly formed by plastic movement of sediment while still saturated. Many beds have flat, eroded tops and complex bottom structures, the latter resulting from loading of flute casts. The reworked sandstone beds display current-ripple or parallel-lamination, and are often composite. Grading can be determined in the foresets and in the laminated beds. The beds are invariably discontinuous or lens like, and show marked thickness variations. Strings of lenses are interpreted as disconnected ripples; in places the ripples are inverted. These beds are believed to be turbidites that have been reworked by persistent sea-bottom currents analogous to contourites in deep ocean basins.

The turbidites and reworked sandstones and coarse siltstones are commonly interbedded, and all may be examined in the craggy outcrop at *Localities 13, 14 and 15*. Generally the silty mudstone is well cleaved and at *Locality 15* a strong tectonic lineation is visible on the bases of the sandstone beds.

Locality 16   At the Old Clogau mine a quartz vein, parallel to that in the Clogau and St David's mines, was worked intermittently mostly for copper from the early 19th century to about 1867. The vein cuts the Maentwrog Formation and parts of the complex, anastomosing system are exposed. In addition to the old shafts, adits and tips, the remains of a horse-whim that is probably unique in Wales is of particular interest.

The route leads from the mine over a stile in a high wall on the north side of a tip along a well-made miners' track.

Locality 17   Cleaved sedimentary and intrusive rocks alongside the stream mark the site of the Bryntirion Fault which downthrows to the east. From here the route follows the well-made path westwards and then takes a minor path that branches to the north-west nearly parallel to the wall. It crosses two old tramways and continues downhill to a gate near *Locality 5*.

High grain concentration at base of graded bed due to shear resistance with substrate.

Convolute lamination

4 Capel Hermon

This is a circular route of about 10 km mainly on forest roads in the upper part of the Afon Wen valley and on the lowest slopes of Rhobell Fawr. It traverses the Rhobell Volcanic Group, the Ffestiniog Flags Formation, high level subvolcanic intrusions and the Coed-y-Brenin porphyry copper deposit. The walk takes about 5 hours. Variations are given for the walker who may wish to leave the main route and visit Llanfachreth. Capel Hermon may be approached from the north or south, in both cases on single track roads with tight bends that will not take large coaches. There is a small Forestry Commission car park [748 256] near the start (Figure 15).

Locality 1 The porphyry copper deposit, proved by Riofinex Ltd in the early 1970s, but not worked, is situated mainly beneath thick boulder clay in the forested valley around Capel Hermon. Details of the deposit are given by Rice and Sharp (1976). The ore deposit consists of chalcopyrite and a little molybdenite both in veinlets and disseminated within a large laccolithic complex of microtonalite and in the roof rocks. The complex was emplaced within the Ffestiniog Flags Formation 0.5 to 1 km below the base of the co-magmatic Rhobell Fawr volcano in late Tremadoc times, and was mineralised in a phase of hydrothermal activity during that volcanic episode. In most porphyry copper deposits there is extensive hydrothermal alteration of the host and the surrounding rocks but the usual pattern of a potassic zone (potash feldspar and biotite) at the core with phyllic zone (mainly sericite) around it and a propylitic zone (chlorite and epidote mainly) on the outside is not developed fully here. The potassic zone has not been recognised with certainty, and the ore-body is associated with phyllic altered rocks.

One of the very few exposures of the ore-body occurs in a forest road cutting about 150 m S of the car park. The rock is intensely sericitised and fractured. Weathering has reduced the copper sulphides to malachite which stains the rock green. In the head deposit which overlies the solid rock, a basal green layer of strong copper enrichment demonstrates the mobility of copper in groundwater systems.

Near the junction of the forest road with the metalled road, about 70 m S of the car park, there are the remains of waste tips from one of the old Dol-frwynog mines in which chalcopyrite-pyrite-bearing quartz veins were tried for gold in the 19th century. Thrift (*Armeria maritima*) grows abundantly in the copper-rich soils here.

Locality 2 This is the site of the old Turf copper mine. In the early 19th century about 70 acres of copper-rich peat were dug, dried and burned to concentrate copper in the ash so that it could be smelted. Most of the peat has been removed, but copper-rich groundwater is still depositing copper

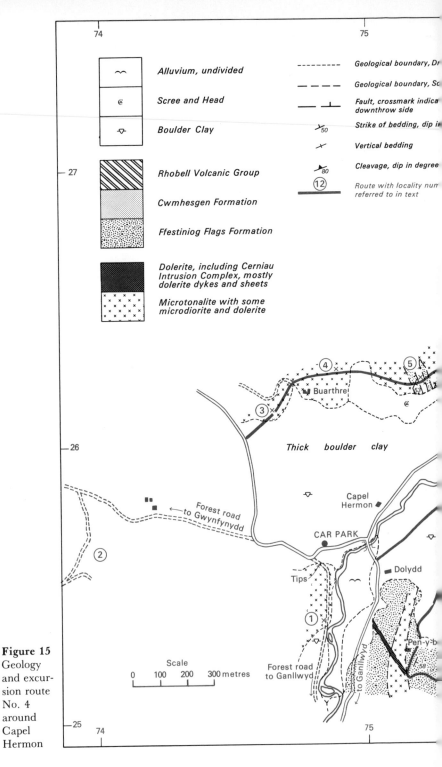

Figure 15 Geology and excursion route No. 4 around Capel Hermon

Legend:

- ~ Alluvium, undivided
- ℮ Scree and Head
- ⌁ Boulder Clay
- Rhobell Volcanic Group
- Cwmhesgen Formation
- Ffestiniog Flags Formation
- Dolerite, including Cerniau Intrusion Complex, mostly dolerite dykes and sheets
- Microtonalite with some microdiorite and dolerite

- - - - - - - Geological boundary, Dr
- - - - - Geological boundary, So
- ——┴— Fault, crossmark indica downthrow side
- ⤡50 Strike of bedding, dip i
- ⤡ Vertical bedding
- ⤡80 Cleavage, dip in degree
- ⑫ Route with locality num referred to in text

Buarthre

Thick   boulder   clay

Forest road to Gwynfynydd

Capel Hermon

CAR PARK

②

Tips

Dolydd

①

Pen-y-b

Scale
0   100   200   300 metres

Forest road to Ganllwyd

to Ganllwyd

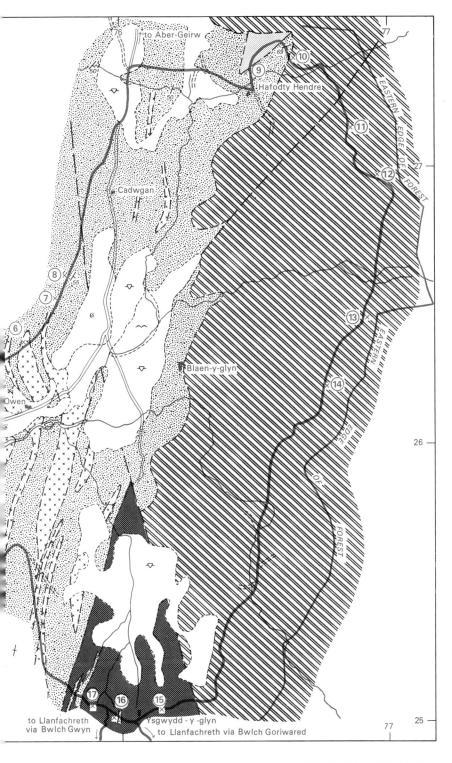

minerals on the sides of drainage ditches. The old Dol-frwynog vein workings reflect some of the efforts the 19th century prospector put into his search for the 'mother lode' from which the copper in the peat was thought to be derived. Ramsay (1866, p. 45), however, had already concluded that the copper was probably finely dispersed through the rock. Riofinex Ltd proved him right over 100 years later.

Localities 3, 4 and 5   On the forest road near Buarthre Cottage there are several large road cuttings in the broad, pyrite-rich zone, commonly referred to as the pyrite halo. At *Locality 3* there is abundant pyrite in both the altered microtonalite and the hard, baked siltstone of the Ffestiniog Flags Formation. It occurs disseminated and in veinlets, in addition to being in quartz veins. Following the forestry road (R132) there are more outcrops at *Localities 4 and 5*. At the latter, a trial level was excavated along a quartz vein in the intrusive microtonalite. About 35 m to the west, baked siltstone contains pyrite in a network fracture system which is typical of this alteration zone.

Locality 6   Here, concordant intrusions of grey micro-tonalite intrude steeply dipping siltstone of the Ffestiniog Flags Formation. The locality is outside the pyrite halo, although the intrusive rocks are altered.

Locality 7   The alternation of thin beds of grey silty mudstone and white, coarse quartzose siltstone or fine sand-stone, which characterises the Ffestiniog Flags Formation, can be examined in an outcrop of steeply dipping beds with small-scale folding. Sedimentary structures include laterally impersistent and lens-shaped bedding, parallel- and cross-lamination, ripple marks, scour-and-fill structures and bur-rows. They indicate deposition in a shallow, probably tidal, environment.

Locality 8   The Ffestiniog Flags Formation is well exposed in this quarry. The formation is not notably fossiliferous, but examples of the brachiopod *Lingulella davisii* can be found here (Figure 16). Like the present-day *Lingula*, this species may have lived in vertical burrows on the sea floor; the examples found here, however, are fragmented and have accumulated at the bases of coarse siltstone beds. An important feature in this quarry is the effect of hillcreep, distorting the true dip in the top 1 to 2 m of solid rock.

From the quarry the forest road more or less follows the strike of the Ffestiniog Flags Formation to the metalled road [7600 2714]. Along this stretch outcrop is abundant and the dips are generally shallower.

Follow the metalled road north and take the rough path to the east, opposite the junction with R24, to join the forest road R212. Turn ESE, and make for the junction with R20 at the ruins of Hafodty-hendre. Turn north on to R20.

Figure 16 *Lingulella davisii* (McCoy) from the Ffestiniog Flags Formation. Ventral valve (on left) and dorsal valve (on right), both × 3

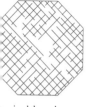

Typical basal section of clinopyroxene crystal

Locality 9 A few metres north on R20, small outcrops of dark grey mudstone occur in the drainage ditch at the roadside. The mudstone is probably of the uppermost Ffestiniog Flags Formation; upwards it becomes darker and pyritic, and passes into the Cwmhesgen Formation.

Locality 10 The base of the Rhobell Volcanic Group is rarely exposed, but its unconformable character is evident from mapping. The group consists of a pile of basaltic lavas and blocky lava breccias erupted subaerially. The lower part of the pile is penetrated by many small intrusions, and it is difficult in places to distinguish in outcrop between the intrusive and extrusive components. In this small outcrop near the base of the pile, blocks of grey siltstones are enclosed in confused relationships within brecciated basalt.

Kokelaar (1979) suggested that the first eruption may have taken place in a shallow marine environment, but the volcano quickly became subaerial. Rhobell Fawr comprises the remains of part of the eastern flank of that volcano. Successively younger lava flows onlap eastwards. The lavas, which range from grey to green in colour consist of two main types: a dominantly grey variety with mostly feldspar and augite phenocrysts, and a darker, green variety with feldspar, large amphibole and less common diopside phenocrysts. In road cuttings immediately south of *Locality 10* the main rock type is the feldspar-rich variety.

Localities 11 to 14 The first appearance of green amphibole-bearing basalt is at *Locality 11*. Locally the rock contains abundant 1 cm pyrite cubes and intricate epidote veining. At *Localities 12 and 14* the basalt is distinctive (Figure 17) with euhedral amphibole phenocrysts up to 2 cm long, and at *Locality 13* the rock displays excellent autoclastic brecciation.

Localities 15 to 17 The feeder zone to the volcano is represented by the Moel y Llan and Cerniau intrusion complexes of mainly basaltic intrusions emplaced along a north-

Figure 17
Amphibole-
bearing basalt

−south fracture system. The complexes are distinguished from each other by the presence of entrapped slabs of Ffestiniog Flags Formation in the Moel y Llan. The Bwlch Goriwared Fault displaces the Cerniau complex against the lava pile, and at *Locality 15*, near the ruins of Ysgwydd-y-glyn, the first of the intrusions in the Cerniau complex may be seen. Though the intrusions are concordant where seen adjacent to sedimentary rock, they are normal to the base of the volcanic pile and are, therefore, dyke-like. Rafts and slivers of baked, pyritised, vertically disposed siltstone of the Ffestiniog Flags Formation trapped between the dykes are exposed at *Locality 16*, which marks the eastern limit of the Moel y Llan complex; westwards the rafts are thicker and more common. West of *Locality 17* sedimentary rocks are more abundant than intrusions. Most of the dykes are basaltic, but among them (e.g. at *Locality 17* and, more commonly, westwards) there are some intrusions of micro-tonalite in the steeply dipping Ffestiniog Flags Formation.

From *Locality 17* follow the forest road downhill past Pen-y-Bryn farm and onwards to rejoin the metalled road near Dolydd.

Two useful variations to this route may be followed. Near the ruins of Ysgwydd-y-glyn between *Localities 15 and 17* two footpaths, one along Bwlch Goriwared and the other over Cerniau, lead to Llanfachreth. Either may be followed, ending the walk at the village, or a circular tour may be made returning to Ysgwydd-y-glyn and thence to Capel Hermon, adding another 2 to 3 hours to the time. Geologically little new is added to the excursion by following these variations, but both of them enable a much more detailed examination to be made of the sub-volcanic Moel y Llan and Cerniau intrusion complexes.

Bwlch Goriwared About 30 m W of Ysgwydd-y-glyn (Figure 18) a narrow track, believed to be part of an old drover's road, leads south-eastwards from the main forest road. It leads out of the forest, and joins a well-made track which runs roughly southwards through Bwlch Goriwared. Llanfachreth is about 3.5 km away.

The bwlch is a strong linear feature, probably along a fault that separates lavas of the Rhobell Volcanic Group on the east from the Cerniau intrusion complex on the west. The lavas and some microtonalite intrusions are well exposed in crags beyond a wall on the east for about 1 km from the forest gate. The Cerniau complex, on the west of the wall, is difficult to resolve. It consists mostly of dolerite with some microtonalite forming an intersecting dyke complex. Some lava remains at the summit of Cerniau, which suggests that the complex is the uppermost part of the feeder dyke zone.

Localities 18 to 20 Grey dolerite with feldspar, pyroxene and amphibole phenocrysts, the latter with white pellicles, crops out in several places (e.g. at *Locality 18*) but, near the old partly blocked trial level at *Locality 19*, green porphyritic dolerite is prevalent. Contacts between these two rocks are present hereabouts, but hard to find. This trial working is one of three in this area. There is a large tip mostly of sparsely pyritised dolerite, but with a few small pieces of mostly crystalline quartz. Farther south, at *Locality 20*, porphyritic dolerite and microtonalite are found in adjacent outcrops.

Cerniau About 150 m W of Ysgwydd-y-glyn a white-topped post marks where a footpath crosses the main forest road. Southwards, the path winds uphill through the forest and emerges at a narrow wooden gate. From here the path to the south crosses craggy moorland. It is quite clear for about 200 m, but then becomes difficult to follow until about 200 m from the gate [7557 2423]. It is advisable before crossing this tract of land to take a compass bearing on the gate.

Locality 21 The Cerniau is arbitrarily separated from the Moel y Llan intrusion complex at the most eastward exposure of enclosed siltstone, but it is possible that the junction is a faulted one. The footpath follows the eastern margin of the Moel y Llan complex which, unlike the Cerniau, is composed of dyke-like intrusions within Ffestiniog Flags Formation. At this locality near the gate is a craggy outcrop of porphyritic dolerite. It is brecciated in parts, possibly by late hydrothermal activity, and a 60-cm thick dyke of dark green fine-grained dolerite cuts the breccia.

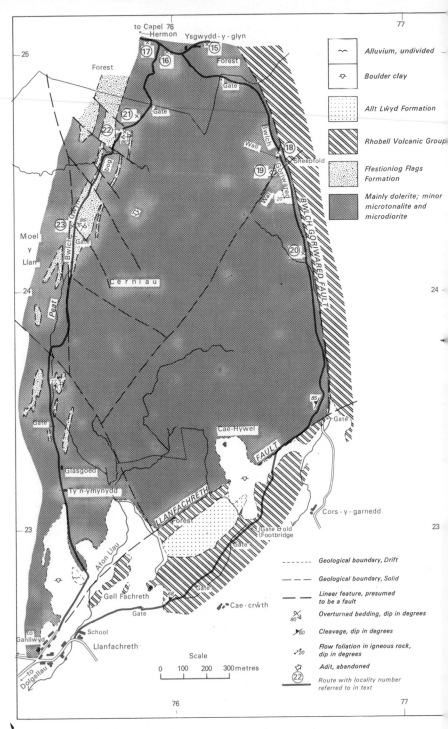

Figure 18 Paths to Llanfachreth over Cerniau and along Bwlch Goriwared

Locality 22   One of many outcrops of steeply dipping, vertical, or overturned baked and cleaved siltstone of the Ffestiniog Flags Formation occurs here.

Locality 23   About 50 m N of the gate [7557 2423] the path rises out of Bwlch Gwyn. The view from here encompasses Rhobell Fawr, the Rhinogs, Foel Offrwn and Cader Idris.

5   Bryn-llin-fawr

The Cwmhesgen Formation is richer in fossils than any of the other Cambrian formations and the main purpose of this excursion is to examine some good fossil localities within it. The route (Figure 19) traverses a section through the formation from the top of the Ffestiniog Flags Formation to the base of the Aran Volcanic Group. The return trip is a little over 8 km of easy walking, mostly along forest roads. The main part of the trail is protected by mature pines, and it may be enjoyed even in the rain. Half a day can easily be spent on it. Some parking space is available near Pont Aber-Geirw on the Afon Mawddach [768 291], which is approached by single-track roads either from Ganllwyd or Bronaber. From the bridge walk uphill to the north and turn right through the gate on the first bend on to a metalled track that leads towards Bryn-llin-fawr farm.

Looking south from the track the valley is floored by boulder clay locally moulded into drumlins, as at Bryn Geirw. Beyond there, leading to the farm, the volcanic rocks of Rhobell Fawr can be seen. Looking eastwards, along the Mawddach valley, the Ordovician Aran Volcanic Group caps the steep scarp of Allt Lŵyd. The track cuts along the base of the scree and several exposures of the Ffestiniog Flags Formation can be seen. About 200 m before the farm, the track leads down to a ford. A section in the boulder clay can be seen adjacent to the ford [7729 2974]. This contains blocks, mainly of shale, and is dark bluish grey, typical of the till derived from the Dolgellau Member. Cross the river and make for the gate [7734 2959] into the forest.

Localities 1 to 4   These localities are in the Ffestiniog Flags Formation and can be located most easily by reference to the fire breaks, shown in Figure 19. At *Locality 1*, close to the gate, the sedimentary structures typical of the formation are well displayed. The dip is to the east and the lowest beds are fairly uniform grey siltstone which split easily along the bedding planes. These pass up into more thickly bedded units, up to about 15 cm, and locally lenses of pale grey quartzose siltstone, with thin beds and laminae of dark siltstone. Cross-stratification is common in the quartzose siltstone; some units show truncated tops, others have well developed ripple marks. Relatively large scale cross-stratification, though difficult to determine in restricted exposures, seems to be present in the eastern part of this cutting. Whole and fragmented specimens of the brachiopod *Lingulella davisii* can be found at this exposure. The fossil bands represent accumulations of shells washed and broken by currents.

Similar lithologies occur in a small exposure at *Locality 2*

[7749 2980], but, higher in the succession, at *Locality 3* [7767 3008], thin beds of dark grey siltstone appear. In the nearly vertical beds at *Locality 4* some bedding planes are covered in micro-ripples. Black *Lingulella* shells are abundant.

Locality 5   A fault, not exposed, crosses the track between *Localities 4 and 5*. The quarry at *Locality 5* is cut into the Dolgellau Member of the Cwmhesgen Formation. The beds are very dark grey to black silty mudstone and have yielded a few specimens of the trilobite *Parabolina spinulosa* (Figure 20).

A small fault, with a breccia zone 7 to 8 cm thick, occurs about 6 m from the east end of the quarry. The fault trends at 161° and hades to the west.

Locality 6   The drain by the side of the forestry track is floored by dark grey mudstone of the Dolgellau Member, which contains an abundance of the small brachipod *Orusia lenticularis* (Figure 20). Unless the drain has recently been cleared the exposure is likely to be covered by fallen debris. *Orusia lenticularis* is generally less than 5 mm across, but it occurs in such numbers here as to cover successive bedding planes through a small thickness of strata.

Locality 7   From the previous locality the track crosses the axis of a shallow anticline. In the quarry at *Locality 7* the uppermost part of the Ffestiniog Flags Formation is exposed on the eastern limb of this anticline. The siltstone is much darker than at *Locality 1* although the same bedding characteristics persist. Exceptionally, for this formation, a single thick bed of silty sandstone shows graded bedding. The beds again yield *Lingulella davisii* and rare examples of the trilobite *Parabolinoides bucephalus* which characterises the top Ffestiniog and basal Dolgellau beds. Some of the bedding surfaces show slickensides produced by flexural slip of adjacent beds during folding.

Locality 8 [7890 3050]   A quarry near the boundary of mature and younger trees exposes a fresh section of the Dolgellau Member. The beds consist of very dark silty mudstone showing grey colour banding, and include scattered phosphatic nodules. The pyritous laminae typical of this member are also present.

Locality 9 [7903 3066]   The section along the track has been cleared by the Nature Conservancy Council, with the permission of the Forestry Commission, as a Site of Special Scientific Interest. The section is cut in the Cwmhesgen Formation through the top of the Dolgellau Member into the lower part of the Dol-cyn-afon Member which, in this area, marks the chronostratigraphical boundary between the Merioneth Series and the Tremadoc Series. A full account of this section is given by Rushton (1982).

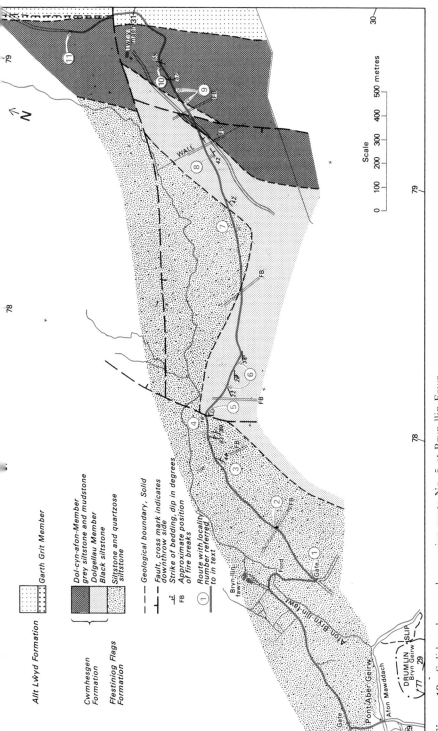

Figure 19 Solid geology and excursion route No. 5 at Bryn-llin-Fawr

Key

Allt Lŵyd Formation

Garth Grit Member

Cwmhesgen Formation
- Dol-cyn-afon-Member grey siltstone and mudstone
- Dolgellau Member Black siltstone

Ffestiniog Flags Formation
- Siltstone and quartzose siltstone

— — Geological boundary, Solid

– – – Fault, cross mark indicates downthrow side

$\underline{}^2$ Strike of bedding, dip in degrees

FB Approximate position of fire breaks

① Route with locality number referred to in text

Moving up the sequence, from south-west to north-east, there is a gradual change in colour from the very dark grey beds of the Dolgellau Member to the rather pale grey siltstone and mudstone of the Dol-cyn-afon Member. This section is not particularly fossiliferous but, with patience and care, it is possible to find fossils of the top biozone of the Merioneth Series, namely the *Acerocare* Zone, and the basal zone of the overlying Tremadoc Series, that of *Dictyonema flabelliforme*. The *Acerocare* Zone yields several trilobites, most commonly *Niobella homfrayi, Parabolina heres* and a *Shumardia*, together with hyolithid molluscs and the brachiopod *Broeggeria* (Figure 20). The Tremadoc yields small varieties of *Dictyonema flabelliforme*, the brachiopod *Eurytreta sabrinae* and a few trilobites. The zones are separated by about a metre of grey mudstone, apparently without fossils. Two 10 cm-thick tuffite beds separated by about 30 cm of grey mudstone occur just below the unfossiliferous beds and serve, in this section, as a lithological marker for the base of the Dol-cyn-afon Member. They contain crystals, mainly feldspar with some bipyramidal quartz, and indicate contemporaneous volcanic activity in the area. The lower bed is cross-stratified, indicating that the volcanic material, which probably settled from an ash cloud, was reworked by currents. Abundant pyrite is concentrated in thin 'veins' at right angles' to the bedding, suggesting that the veins mark dewatering channels in the sediment.

Locality 10 [7916 3081]   The beds are typical of the Dol-cyn-afon Member. They are paler grey than the Dolgellau Member with some dark grey bands. Scattered black phosphatic nodules, up to about 1 cm long, and interbedded sandy bands and laminae occur in places. These sandy bands are characteristic of the Dol-cyn-afon Member in this area and consist of pellets of recrystallised chlorite. The beds yield *Dictyonema flabelliforme* in slightly more abundance and in a better state of preservation than the previous locality.

Locality 11 [7920 3024]   The large quarry is excavated in the Dol-cyn-afon Member in a lithology similar to that seen at the previous locality. A careful search, particularly among the weathered slabs may yield some trilobites: several varieties have been found and *Niobella homfrayi smithi, Micragnostus* cf. *bavaricus* and *Proteuloma* cf. *geinitzi* are the commonest, together with large hyolithids; they represent a low Tremadoc horizon.

Exposure continues along the track and, near where a small stream crosses it, [7917 3048] the coarse-grained quartzose sandstone of the Garth Grit Member, which marks the base of the Ordovician Aran Volcanic Group, is exposed on the east side of the track.

Figure 20
Fossils from the Dolgellau Member
1 *Peltura scarabaeoides* (Wahlenberg), × 3, from the *P. scarabaeoides* Zone.
2 *Parabolina spinulosa* (Wahlenberg), × 3, from the *P. spinulosa* Zone.
3 *Broeggeria salteri* (Holl), ventral valve, × 3, from the *Acerocare* Zone.
4 *Niobella homfrayi* (Salter), × 2, from the *Acerocare* Zone.
5 *Orusia lenticularis* (Wahlenberg), × 3, from the *P. spinulosa* Zone.
6 *Parabolina heres* Brögger, × 3, from the *Acerocare* Zone.

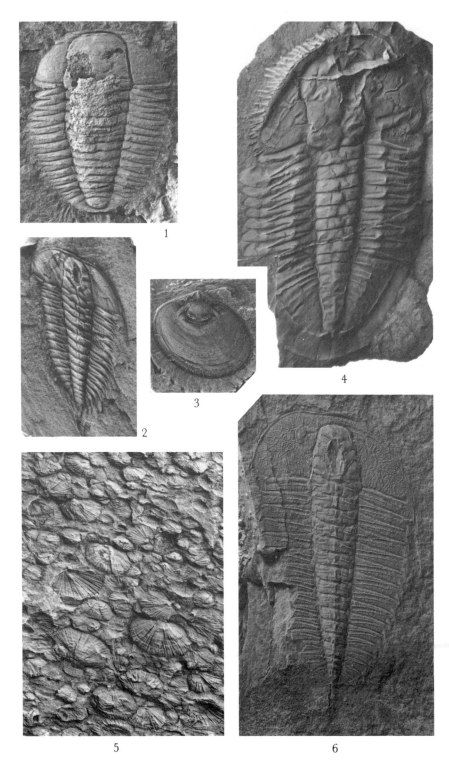

6   Allt Lŵyd

The route (Figure 21) follows the Afon Cwmhesgen, a tributary of the Afon Mawddach, and crosses most of the formations of the Ordovician Aran Volcanic Group. The footpath is not well defined but most of the localities are along the stream, which is easy to follow. The return trip is about 5 km and the route climbs from 270 m to about 490 m OD. As with Excursion 5 the start of this route may be approached either from Bronaber or Ganllwyd. About 500 m S of Pont Aber-Geirw [7685 2870] a road marked as a cul-de-sac runs east-north-east into Cwm yr Allt-lŵyd. Follow this road for about 2 km and park at the roadside near the bridge where the metalled road ends. Cross the bridge and follow the track towards Cwmhesgen farm [7868 2955].

The classic U-shaped profile of Cwm yr Allt-lŵyd clearly indicates the effect of glacial erosion. It is floored by alluvium on boulder clay, which is thick near Cwmhesgen. On the north side of the river, about 200 m W of the bridge, a large landslip in the boulder clay shows the typical crescentic rim and hummocky surface.

On the north-east side of the valley the steep scarp is mantled by thick scree and capped by Ordovician volcanogenic rocks. On the south and south-west, the upper Cambrian Cwmhesgen Formation forms the more rounded topography in the foreground with the Ffestiniog Flags Formation in the small crags above the road and east of Rhiw-Felen. The Rhobell Volcanic Group forms the craggier topography. Large glacial erratics are scattered in the stream and on the valley sides.

Although this excursion is about Ordovician rocks it is worthwhile looking at the roadside adjacent to the parking position where dark, locally fossiliferous shales of the Dolgellau Member (Excursion 5) are exposed. In the river bed at the eastern end of the landslip is the type locality for the base of the Cwmhesgen Formation. Here dark grey flaggy mudstone of the Dolgellau Member rests with abrupt colour change on paler grey siltstone of the Ffestiniog Flags Formation.

The public footpath leaves the farm track just before entering the farmyard and crosses the field to a gate, though there is no evidence of it on the ground. Beyond the gate the path follows the base of a head deposit and is marked, at intervals, by large boulders. The smooth rounded hill on the north side of the stream is in shales of the Cwmhesgen Formation. The line of low crags on the eastern side marks the base of the Ordovician (Aran Volcanic Group) and this can be traced downhill to a waterfall.

Locality 1 [7960 3008] A sequence of very dark grey siltstone with contrasting ribs of pale grey sandstone, typical of the lower part of the Allt Lŵyd Formation, the lowest formation in the Aran Volcanic Group, is exposed in the water-

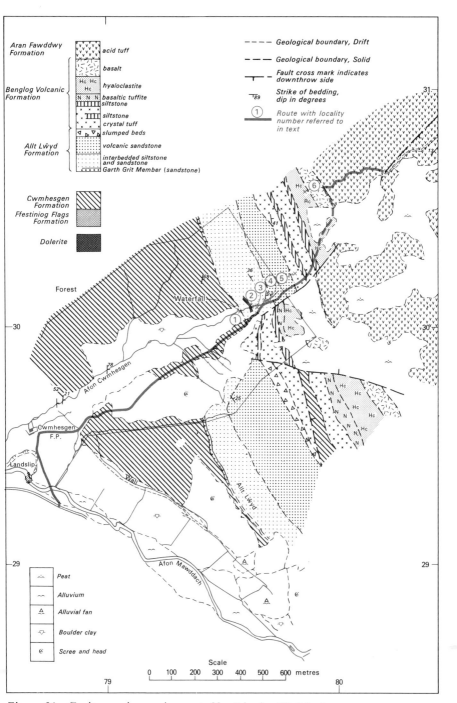

Figure 21 Geology and excursion route No. 6 in the Allt Lŵyd area

fall. The Garth Grit Member, which is the lowest unit of this formation, is just visible below the siltstones on the south bank of the river, adjacent to the gully. This member is thin but distinctive. It is a pale grey, coarse-grained sandstone, consisting predominantly of quartz and quartzite grains. Here the sandstone is about 70 cm thick, with grains 1 to 3 mm in diameter in a brown-weathering cement.

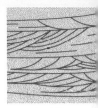

Cross bedding

The overlying banded sedimentary rocks are much finer grained, but several thicker beds of greenish grey impure sandstone occur, one of these forming the lip of the waterfall. The banded beds, which are the dominant lithology here, are interpreted as sediments deposited in a tidal environment where the accumulation of mud and silt was interrupted periodically by currents carrying fine sand. The sand was subsequently reworked and winnowed, and the beds now show a variety of sedimentary features including parallel-and cross-lamination, ripple marks and sand injection structures (Figure 22). Although fossils are not common, the evidence suggests that the environment supported a prolific fauna. Burrows, preserved by an infill of fine sand, are abundant, and some levels show a chaotic internal structure (bioturbation) where the sediment has been disturbed by feeding and burrowing animals.

Locality 2 [7963 3008]   At the low waterfall, a sill, about 1 m thick, is composed of fine-grained dolerite which is highly vesicular towards the top. Vesicles are filled with calcite. At the top the sill is slightly discordant, cutting across the overlying beds. There is little evidence of contact metamorphism.

Upstream, the banded beds first seen at *Locality 1* continue with a gradual increase in the number of sandstone beds.

Locality 3   A vesicular dolerite intrusion (4.5 m thick) cuts black siltstone. The siltstone is tuffaceous in places, containing crystal debris derived from volcanic ash. Additionally there is an oolitic ironstone unit about 4 m thick. It consists of golden yellow ooliths of pyrite in a dark silty groundmass. These rocks, including the intrusion, contain much disseminated pyrite. Above this outcrop, an exposure gap of 6 or 7 m is followed by a rather poor exposure of tuffite consisting almost entirely of angular clasts and crystals of volcanic origin and overlain by a compact, heterogeneous breccia. The upper part of the formation is dominated by coarse-grained, reworked volcaniclastic rocks. The tuffite and breccia here, therefore, mark a pulse of volcanic activity preceding the main volcanic episode.

Oolitic ironstone. Alternating bands of pyrite, quartz and chlorite form around nucleii of altered feldspar crystals. /

Locality 4   Due north, across the broken wall from the previous locality is a low crag of volcanic sandstone typical of the upper part of the Allt Lŵyd Formation. The rock is coarse-grained, grey, thickly bedded with parallel- and cross-

A

2cm

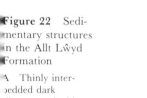

Figure 22 Sedimentary structures in the Allt Lŵyd Formation

A Thinly interbedded dark siltstone and white sandstone show typical turbulence structures.
B A vertical burrow cross-cuts bioturbated siltstone and sandstone.

B

2cm

stratification, and consists of feldspar crystals or fragments of porphyry derived from volcanic ash and redeposited in a fluviatile or deltaic environment. The unit of volcanic sandstone, which is gradational with the underlying banded siltstone and sandstone unit, is relatively thin here and partially concealed under boulder clay.

From the head of the valley one can see Rhinog Fawr, Rhinog Fach, Y Llethyr and Diffwys to the west. The long ridge in the middle distance is developed on the relatively hard Ffestiniog Flags Formation while the shales of the Cwmhesgen Formation form smoother rounded slopes. On the north of the valley the top of Craig y Dinas protruding above the forest is capped by an outlier of lavas of the Rhobell Volcanic Group which crop out more extensively to the south on Rhobell y Big and Rhobell Fawr.

Follow the wall and poorly defined path through the fence bearing to the left.

Locality 5 The crystal tuff comprising the Benglog Volcanic Formation is one of the most uniform in the group, and can be traced from Moel Llyfnant in the north to the slopes of

Cader Idris in the south. It is a massive rock made up almost exclusively of large sericitised feldspar crystals in a matrix of chlorite or sericite. Other clasts include microtonalite, scoria and dark siltstone, similar to that of the Dolgellau Member and the tuffs are probably mass-flow deposits derived from volcanic debris accumulated on unstable slopes. The tuff is divided into an upper and lower unit by a thin band of siltstone containing scattered feldspar crystals which is exposed in the hollow between them (Figure 21). The upper unit is overlain by a similar thin tuffaceous siltstone.

Locality 6   Basic lavas form a rounded feature to the north of the small patch of peat. The lower part is brecciated, consisting of blocks of pale grey vesicular basalt in a dark glassy groundmass, and includes siltstone fragments incorporated by the moving lava from the substrate. The texture of the basalt fragments suggests that brecciation was facilitated by the rapid quenching of the molten lava, probably in contact with water, and thus this rock could be termed a hyaloclastite. To the east the hyaloclastite passes into a more massive uniform basalt which is greenish grey and medium grained, with numerous vesicles infilled with chlorite, calcite or quartz. Calcite veins cut the basalt. The upper unit of this flow, exposed at the back of the sheep-pen, is pillowed (Figure 23). The ovoid pillows have alternating concentric bands of vesicular and non-vesicular basalt and are surrounded by a fine vesicular glass. The formation of pillow lavas generally results from lava flowing over a topographic irregularity under water. The lavas are separated by a topographic depression from the overlying acid ash-flow tuffs of the Aran Fawddwy Formation, the uppermost of the Aran

Figure 23   Pillow lava

Volcanic Group in this area. The tuffs, which are more silica-rich than the crystal tuffs of the Benglog Volcanic Formation, form the high ground in the east. They show the bleached surface typical of acid tuffs. They are massive and fairly uniform, consisting of scattered feldspar crystals and a few lithic clasts in a grey homogeneous groundmass, which in thin section show numerous cuspate devitrified shards, representing fragments of vesicular glass.

From the top of the hill, where the panorama encompasses the major peaks of North Wales, the right of way passes into the valley of the Afon Lliw and then to Llanuwchllyn.

7 Upper Afon Melau valley

This circular route of about 7 km, across the core of the Melau anticline immediately south of Rhobell Fawr, (Figure 24) traverses the upper part of the Mawddach Group, a short section through the Rhobell Volcanic Group and the lower part of the Ordovician sequence; it thus covers the same formations as Excursions 4, 5 and 6. The route, mostly along forest roads and good tracks, ranges in elevation from 270 to 460 m OD and should take about half a day. The simplest approach is to follow a minor road signed to Llanfachreth from the Bala to Dolgellau road (A494), about 0.5 km E of the junction with the Brithdir road (B4416). Pass straight through the first cross-roads. The road ahead is gated. At the second cross-roads continue straight on, taking the route marked as a 'cul de sac'. From the cross-roads, the road, though largely unmetalled, is passable by car for at least 1 km, but it may be preferable to park near this junction, taking care not to obstruct access to fields, and walk.

Locality 1 [7830 2338] At this old slate working in the Ffestiniog Flags Formation, waste tips occur at two levels near the main adits. One of the adits is on the west of the road just beyond a small ruined building. At this adit the sedimentary features show up clearly on the weathered cleavage surfaces. The cleavage dips at an angle steeper than the bedding. At the mouth of the adit a 40-cm bed of pale grey, fine, quartzose sandstone shows large scale trough cross-stratification, which is rarely seen in natural exposure as the beds tend to break away into flaggy slabs. This is interbedded with alternating beds of grey and pale grey quartzose siltstone. Uphill, above the adit, several trials occur north of the air shaft, where the beds have been worked along strike thus providing a surface on which the lateral variation in the rocks can be examined. The pale quartzose beds show parallel- and cross-stratification, the latter in units as little as 0.5 cm thick. Both these and the thicker units can be seen to die out along the strike. The crags at the top of the hill mark a dolerite intrusion.

Locality 2 [7843 2406] From the quarries the road leads through the forestry area NNW to this exposure by the track side. It is cleaved grey uniform siltstone with sparse quartzose laminae, and is close to the top of the Ffestiniog Flags Formation. Upwards there is a gradual change in colour from fairly uniform mid-grey siltstone to very dark grey and black. The stream section to the north has yielded the typical fossils *Parabolina spinulosa* and *Orusia lenticularis* (Figure 20).

Locality 3 [7837 2410]   Beds here consist of dark grey siltstone, but through the gate behind the wall on the left [7832 2412] a shallow quarry is cut in black banded silty mudstone typical of the Dolgellau Member of the Cwmhesgen Formation.

Locality 4 [7829 2414]   The crags exposed on the right bank of the stream are not typical of the Dolgellau Member. They are massive and compact, resulting from baking at the contact of the large coarse-grained dolerite intrusion. The dolerite forms the steep scarp to the north of the river and blocks of it may be examined in the scree and in the adjacent stone walls. More exposures occur at the top of the ridge [7834 2426 and 7839 2423].

Locality 5 [7849 2428]   Here, the pale grey laminated siltstone of the Ffestiniog Flags Formation exposed on the path is metamorphosed near the contact with the dolerite, which is exposed farther along the path [7859 2434].

Locality 6 [7884 2463]   Through the fence, the Rhobell Volcanic Group forms the steep scarp to the west. Where the track passes through the next wall, large blocks of lava occur adjacent to the path. Above the crag the lavas are generally massive and uniform, but lenses of breccia can be seen. The lavas contain an abundance of feldspar phenocrysts, 2 to 3 mm long, in a dark green groundmass. To the north-east, several minor faults displace medium grey shales of the Dol-cyn-afon Member [7892 2469] on to the ridge. Farther to the east the ridge passes back on to the Rhobell Volcanic Group, and on Graig Fach, in the crags immediately to the east of the wall [7916 2483], there are intercalated breccias in which large irregular blocks, up to 60 cm across, are contained in a feldspar-rich basaltic matrix. On the eastern face of Graig Fach the contact of the lavas with the shales of the Cwmhesgen Formation dips to the west.

Locality 7 [7937 2468]   The low feature here forms the contact between the two members of the Cwmhesgen Formation. The colour change from the lower darker grey shales to the medium grey hues of the upper member is gradual.

The track to the north-east swings eastwards through the forest which lies on the outcrop of the Dolgellau Member, here forming the core of the Melau anticline.

Locality 8 [7971 2464]   This quarry has been used by the Forestry Commission for roadstone. The beds near the base of the Dol-cyn-afon Member are dark grey shales with a

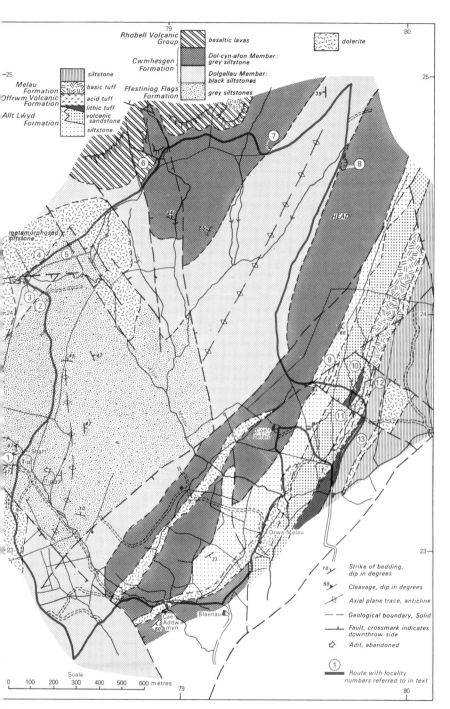

Figure 24 Geology and excursion route No. 7 in the Upper Afon Melau valley

faintly defined lamination and a platy parting. They contain a sparse fauna diagnostic of the Tremadoc Series, including sponge spicules, *Eurytreta* cf. *sabrinae*, a hyolithid and bellerophontid, *Niobella, Shumardia* and *Dictyonema flabelliforme* cf. *sociale*. At the southern end of the quarry, 1 to 2 m of head (loose debris carried down slope by solifluction processes) overlies the solid rock.

Southwards along the track a few exposures appear through head, and fragments of *Dictyonema flabelliforme* may be found.

On the eastern limb of the Melau anticline the road crosses on to the lowest part of the Aran Volcanic Group. There is some discordance in dip between the Cambrian and Ordovician rocks in the Cae'r-defaid area, but both dip to the east. The Aran Volcanic Group seen here is quite different from the section in the Cwmhesgen valley (Excursion No. 6). The road gives access only to the lower part of the group.

Locality 9 [7961 2372]   The Garth Grit Member, which marks the base of the Allt Lŵyd Formation to the north, is not seen here, and the lowest exposed beds are banded dark grey siltstone with thin pale laminae (p. 40). Moving eastwards, up the succession, beds of pale grey feldspathic sandstone are intercalated with the siltstones, but the well-developed cleavage obscures the sedimentary structure.

Through the gate and to the north of the fence, the crags adjacent to the track are thickly bedded coarse-grained sand-stone made up of feldspar crystals and lithic fragments. Locally the beds show parallel- and cross-stratification. The dark siltstones are absent here.

Locality 10 [7977 2368]   The roadside exposure, still within the Allt Lŵyd Formation, is of tuffite, which consists almost entirely of lapilli of feldspar-porphyry. The beds are crudely graded, and show parallel- and cross-lamination that indicate reworking of the sediment by water. A bed of fine vitric tuff 20 to 30 cm thick, overlies the coarse beds.

Locality 11   The stream crossing the road follows an outcrop of a softer-weathering basalt. In the exposure to the south of the road the basalt shows good columnar jointing.

Locality 12 [7983 2366]   Acid tuffs, characteristically bleach-ed, occur here at the feather edge of the Offrwm Volcanic Formation, which is thicker to the south-west. The tuffs are fine-grained, but contain some scattered crystals and clasts and show a well-developed banding in places. This banding is commonly seen in the reworked tops of the ash-flow units and its presence suggests that this is the distal part of the original flow.

The acid tuff is overlain by a thin horizon of crystal-rich or tuffaceous siltstone, but northwards along strike basic tuff occupies this position. The rubbly basic tuff, exposed in the field to the north [7993 2393], consists of fragments of scoria, or highly vesiculated basalt, in a matrix of chlorite and calcite.

Locality 13   The Benglog Volcanic Formation, which crops out on Craig y Benglog to the north-east of this area, is underlain by a thick siltstone unit above the Allt Lŵyd, Offrwm and Melau formations. It is exposed to the east of the road where this turns downhill to the south. The medium grey siltstone contains laminae and thin beds of crystals and crystal pseudomorphs, which indicate continuing contemporaneous volcanism. The cleavage is almost at right angles to the bedding and makes a search for fossils very difficult.

From the road, turn west towards Cae'r-defaid cottage where the footpath to the south passes into the Forestry Commission area, then downhill to the Afon Melau. Continue SSW along the wall, and follow the farm tracks to Drws-Melau and Cae-Addw-wyn. From Cae-Addw-wyn the footpath is not well marked but follows the stream westwards, veering south-west where it passes through a wall, past a ruined barn, and then uphill back to the track (Figure 24).

8   Llandanwg

Although there is abundant evidence of the erosional effects of glaciation in this part of Wales, the deposits from the glaciers are not particularly well exposed. Boulder clay is the most widespread, filling the valley floors and exposed along the river banks. Fluvioglacial sediments deposited from melt-water are not particularly common. However, on a short walk along the coast at Llandanwg both can be seen, together with several other interesting glacial and more modern features.

Trains stop at Llandanwg Halt (Figure 25), but for road users there is a car park at the end of the road adjacent to the beach. From there one can see the effects of contemporary geological processes, where the small church of St Tanwg's is partially buried by blown sand forming the dunes and has to be dug out at regular intervals. To the south the channel of Afon Artro is steadily silting up so that, without dredging, it would leave the Pensarn yacht club high and dry. Northwards along the coast, the boulder clay cliff is protected to some extent from the erosive influence of the sea by the railway embankment. However fluvioglacial gravels along the back of the beach at Llandanwg, though normally covered by vegetation and fallen debris, are commonly exposed in recent landslip scars.

Northwards along the beach from the car park, the sand dunes wedge out abruptly against the gravels and boulder clay. Recent slip scars show bedded gravel resting on boulder

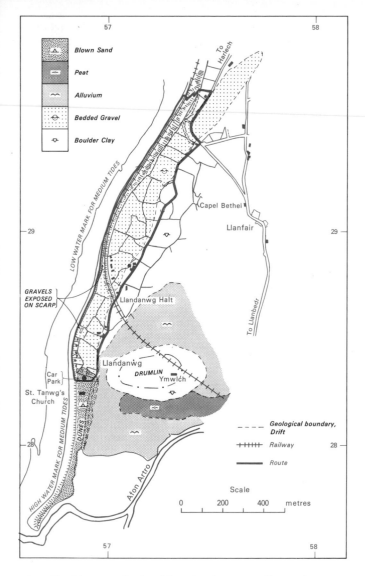

Figure 25
Geology and excursion route No 8 around Llandanwg

clay. In this area the boulder clay is unusually sandy, containing unsorted boulders and cobbles in a pebbly sandy matrix with little clay. Boulders are mainly locally-derived Cambrian greywacke and shale with a few exotic quartzite and microgranite. The matrix may have a ferruginous or manganiferous cement.

The overlying gravels are bedded and locally cross-stratified, showing that the sediments have been sorted and reworked by water. The gravels are coarse and variable in composition, generally with boulders, cobbles and pebbles in a sandy matrix, with interleaved lenses and thin beds of clean dark brown sand.

From the north end of the beach section [5697 2888] it is possible to walk along the retaining wall west of the railway (there is, however, a fine of 40/- (sic) for trespassing on the railway itself) to see this succession of gravel on boulder clay repeated in the cutting to the east.

In plan the gravels form a linear deposit extending uphill to the north-east into a small valley that served to drain away melt-water from the glacier which occupied the Dwyryd valley. The gravels are the outwash delta-like deposit from this temporary stream.

A footpath crosses the railway [5738 2963] leading uphill through National Trust property to the road. From here the dunes fronting the sands of Morfa Harlech can be seen, with Snowdonia to the north and the Lleyn Peninsula across Tremadoc Bay to the west.

3 Geological notes on popular walks

A large number of footpaths around the Harlech dome are used by many of the visitors who come here every year. On all of them there is something of geological interest, but some give access to particular geological features, such as old mines, or allow the examination of stratigraphical variations of sections covered by the specific excursions detailed above. Nine of these are described below. Some can be used as substitutes for excursions given in the previous section, and others are complementary. Specifically, the Roman Steps offers an opportunity to examine the Rhinog Formation; the Barmouth to Hafotty mines walk can substitute for Excursion 2; someone wishing to examine in detail the Gamlan Formation can find much of interest on the Dolgefeiliau to Gwynfynydd walk; the Panorama Walk can be used as an extension to Excursion 2 to examine the Mawddach Group; the Ffestiniog Flags Formation is magnificently exposed on Precipice Walk, and Torrent Walk offers a complete section through an outlier of the Rhobell Volcanic Group.

9 Barmouth to Hafotty mines

This is one of the popular walks out of Barmouth. The footpath starts with a flight of steep steps leaving the main road between the Last Inn and Porkington Terrace above the entrance to the railway tunnel [6173 1559]. It runs (Figure 26) roughly north, on the east side of Garn, towards the Hafotty mines and curves west to Fronoleu Villas on the main road 2.5 km N of Barmouth; to the villas the path is about 7.5 km. It rises from sea level to a high point of 290 m OD at Bwlch y Llan. The steepest climb is at the start, where the path rises 90 m in 300 m. The path is well marked and offers some splendid views. It covers the same geological features as Excursion 2, but provides a better opportunity to examine the old manganese mines.

Locality 1   At the top of the steps, the old quarry to the west provides a nesting gallery for seagulls as well as a fine section through the top of the Barmouth Formation and the lower part of the Gamlan Formation. The Barmouth Formation, exposed on the west face, consists of thickly bedded, coarse-grained turbidites. The beds are well defined, and many of the characteristic features of turbidites may be examined. There are few interbedded siltstone beds but, in the overlying Gamlan Formation on the north-east of the quarry,

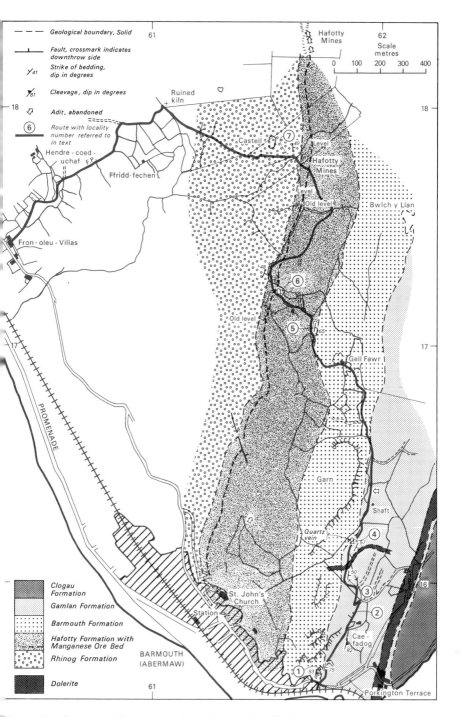

Figure 26 Geology of the footpath from Barmouth to Hafotty manganese mines (No. 9)

banded siltstone and fine-grained sandstone are the main rock types.

The footpath from the quarry leads uphill towards Caefadog. The Gamlan Formation is exposed along the way.

Locality 2 [6188 1688]   A larger outcrop of banded siltstone and mudstone of the Gamlan Formation contains two very pale grey tuff beds, 1.5 and 3 cm thick. The beds are graded, and are interpreted as representing air-fall material that settled from a cloud of volcanic dust. This outcrop also illustrates the variation in the angle of the cleavage (refraction) in passing from coarse to fine-grained beds.

Pass through the gate, bear sharply south-west then north and follow the path uphill through the gate in the wall.

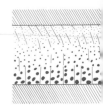

Refracted cleavage in a graded bed

Locality 3 [6186 1603]   To the east of the path on the bend, a 50-cm thick, coarse-grained greywacke bed of a type which occurs locally interbedded with the siltstone in the Gamlan Formation is exposed.

To the north, the beds of the Barmouth Formation can be seen dipping steeply to the east in the crags on Garn, which contrast sharply with the gentler topography formed by the Gamlan Formation. The path lies close to the junction of the two formations.

Locality 4 [6183 1606]   A small tip marks the entrance to a trial in a quartz vein. The vein strikes obliquely across the junction of the two formations, is about a metre wide, and has in association numerous thinner veins cutting the adjacent country rock. Approximately 200 m to the north another small tip marks the location of a shaft [6192 1631] which is probably within the same vein.

Northwards the path follows the junction of the Barmouth and Hafotty formations and provides excellent views of the surrounding mountains. Where the path joins the tarmac road, turn left. Uphill, the route traverses down the succession through the Barmouth Formation. Initially the beds are very thick, coarse-grained sandstones with little interbedded siltstone. Locally [6191 1659] the sandstones are conglomeratic with quartzite pebbles up to 1.5 cm long. Lower in the sequence the rocks are finer grained, more obviously graded and the bedding is more clearly defined. West of the path a small peaty flat may represent an old lake. Beyond the gate [6193 1683] the path continues on the Barmouth Formation. An examination of the crags shows a number of sedimentary cycles, determined on the variation in bedding thickness, grain size and presence of 'Bouma intervals' (p. 15). In each cycle the beds become thinner, there is more siltstone and the turbidites are more complete upwards.

The path crosses the base [6170 1704] of the Barmouth Formation north-west of Gell Fawr.

Locality 5 [6171 1707]   At the crest of the hill the banded siltstone at the top of the Hafotty Formation is exposed. The grey siltstone includes thin, parallel- and cross-laminated sandstone, about 0.5 cm thick. Cleavage dips steeply to the east, and is best developed in the finer-grained lithologies. The contact between the Hafotty and Barmouth formations follows the slack to the right of the path, which bears left through the walls. The grassy ground to the south, occupied by siltstone of the Hafotty Formation, contrasts markedly with the craggy features of the sandstone of the Barmouth Formation on the east and Rhinog Formation on the west.

Locality 6 [6155 1724]   A small trial exposes manganese-bearing shales of the Hafotty Formation, which are more thinly and evenly bedded than the adjacent shales. Cleavage and weathering have produced a rather hackly, broken exposure. The manganese shales contain spessartine nodules, and are distinctly weathered with a purplish brown parting. Along strike to the south another trial occurs in the ore-bed. As elsewhere along the western side of the Harlech dome, the manganese-bearing horizon is overlain by several greywacke beds.

The path continues to the north on the Hafotty Formation to the Hafotty Mine. The abandoned workings lie mainly to the west of the path and the remains of an incline [6159 1779], which served the mines, can also be seen. On the skyline to the north a distinct V marks the position of the workings. The excavation, with associated tips, can be followed downhill along the outcrop.

Locality 7 [6159 1781]   The path now descends the slope, and sandstones of the Rhinog Formation are exposed on either side. The sandstone is thickly bedded, very coarse-grained and includes many pink quartz grains in addition to the ubiquitous white quartzite grains typical of the lower formations of the Harlech Grits Group.

Farther downhill the formation is overlain by head and boulder clay, the latter moulded into a drumlin-like form on Ffridd Fechan. To the south-west a small peat-filled lake basin is visible.

Following the old mine track downhill, the remains of a kiln can be seen just above the wall [6106·1802]. The path descends to the main road. Turn left for Barmouth, but for a more pleasant walk turn right to the post-office and then left to return along the beach and the promenade to Barmouth.

10   Panorama Walk

This highly popular, short, easy walk may be used as an extension of Excursion 2 to examine the lowest parts of the Mawddach Group and some of the numerous sill-like intrusions which lie within the group. Access to Panorama Walk is from Panorama Hill, which rises steeply from the Barmouth–Dolgellau road [6194 1563] near

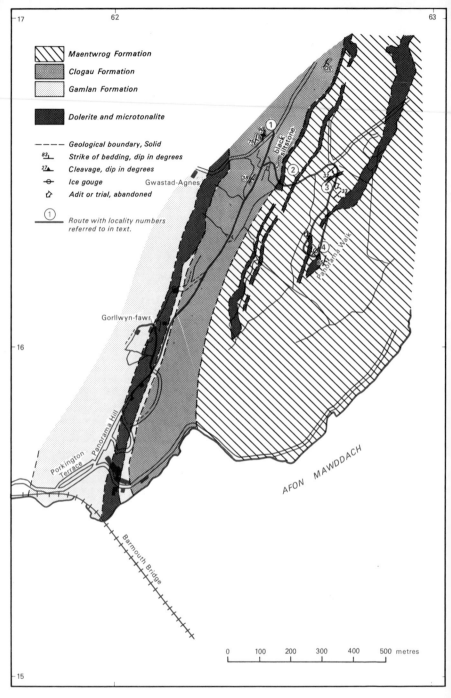

Figure 27 Panorama Walk, geology and footpath (No. 10)

the railway bridge in Barmouth. It is well sign-posted. The start of the footpath leading to Panorama Walk (Figure 27) crosses a long, straight dry valley of glacial origin.

Locality 1 [6250 1667]   The road cutting, not actually on the walk, is worth a visit to examine the typical dark grey to black silty mudstone of the Clogau Formation. The dip is variable, and there is a well-developed cleavage. The Clogau is the lowest carbonaceous formation in the Cambrian succession in North Wales. In places it has yielded many fossils, though none has been found here.

Locality 2 [6254 1650]   Exposed on the path and on the knoll to the north are cleaved, flaggy, medium grey, laminated silty mudstone and coarse quartzose siltstone, together with some thicker greywacke beds at the base of the Maentwrog Formation.

The locally flinty appearance of these rocks is the result of contact metamorphism caused by the dolerite intrusion which forms the south-eastern face of the knoll. The sedimentary characteristics of the formation, described in Excursion 3 (p. 24), may be observed in rocks at this and subsequent localities.

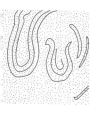

Locality 3   From the gate [6268 1655] to the top of Panorama Hill a typical sequence through the lower part of the south-eastward dipping Maentwrog Formation can be examined. Weathering has accentuated the sedimentary structures in the coarse quartzose siltstone and fine sandstone beds, and there are some excellent examples of parallel-, cross- and convolute-lamination and slumping.

Slumped beds

A number of dolerite sills, some of which are coarse-grained, intrude the sedimentary rocks, and stand out as more blocky exposures usually with regular, evenly spaced joints.

A small, collapsed trial-working lies to the east of the path [6270 1649]. It is one of several old workings hereabouts, all part of Panorama Mine. The trials in quartz-sulphide veins were first worked in 1887, and from 1900 to 1924 Isaac Storey put a great deal of effort and money into his search for gold in this area. The main adit was driven by him from the east into the hillside below Panorama Walk. It intersected six quartz veins containing chalcopyrite, galena, sphalerite, pyrite and pyrrhotite, but there is no record of gold having been found.

Locality 4   Near the farthest point of the path [6264 1628] is a distinctive hollow, possibly classifiable as a p-form, about 10 m in length, 30 cm deep and with a smooth ribbed surface. It trends north-east (Figure 28) and was possibly carved by boulders entrapped in the ice at the base of the glacier that occupied the valley during the last Ice Age. Near the peak is a large, angular erratic of pebbly greywacke, probably de-

Figure 28   Sketch of ice-scour gouge on Panorama Walk

rived from the outcrop of the Barmouth or Rhinog formations in the centre of the Harlech dome.

South-east of the summit [6260 1634] another trial pit has been dug along two quartz veins containing small amounts of galena. From here, most of the formations of the Cambrian succession of the Harlech dome can be picked out. To the north-west the greywackes of the Barmouth Formation form the craggy summit of Garn, and the shales of the Gamlan Formation form the lower grassy slopes. The lowest ground, now followed by the minor road leading to Panorama Walk and Sylfaen, lies in soft mudstones of the Clogau Formation. South-east across the estuary, the Ffestiniog Flags Formation crops out at Penmaenpool and Fegla Fach, while the slate tips farther to the west lie in the Cwmhesgen Formation. Dolerite intrusions form the hills behind the slate workings. Beyond them the Cader Idris range is built of volcanic rocks of Ordovician age.

Along the north-west side of the circuit another small adit along the margin of the dolerite sill can be examined. Near the contact the beds are folded into a small anticline and syncline.

11   Roman Steps (Bwlch Tyddiad)

This popular tourist haunt is easily accessible by car, though it is possible to pick a route to it along the numerous public footpaths leading out of Llanbedr. The woodlands provide a habitat for a wide variety of birds, including woodpeckers. During the summer, if there is heavy traffic, walking along the road may not be pleasant.

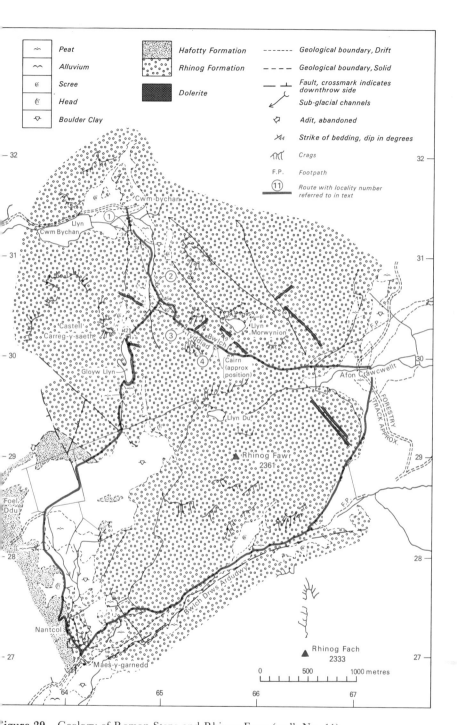

Figure 29 Geology of Roman Steps and Rhinog Fawr (walk No. 11)
The 'steps' occur at intervals between localities 2 and 4

The road runs east from Victoria Inn on the A496 at Llanbedr along the north bank of the Afon Artro, to Cwm Bychan at the head of the valley, where a small fee is charged for parking. The walk to the top of the col is about 2.5 km and rises 280 m. From there paths lead eastwards to Bronaber, about 5.5 km away, or back to the car park on rough paths round Rhinog Fawr (p. 59).

The course of the River Artro is controlled by faults over much of its length, and for most of the route the Rhinog Formation crops out on the hills to the south-east while the Rhinog, Hafotty and Barmouth formations occur in a generally NW dipping sequence to the north-west of the faults. Approaching Cwm Bychan the road curves east, passing over massive greywackes of the Rhinog Formation. The lake lies along the line of a small fault in a deep basin carved into gently dipping sandstones of the Rhinog Formation.

From the car park, follow the footpath across the Afon Artro (Figure 29). The flat wet ground to the east is probably lacustrine alluvium, the rock bar which carries the footpath having once acted as a dam ponding the river in the basin which has now been silted up with sediment.

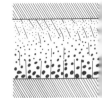

Refracted cleavage in a graded bed

Locality 1 The greywackes of the Rhinog Formation are thickly bedded, jointed, coarse-grained and pebbly, consisting of quartz, feldspar and rock fragments. Most of the beds show a graded lower part and fine-grained top (intervals '*ae*', p. 15). The main fracture cleavage consists of closely spaced, parallel fracture planes. Cleavage refraction (p. 52) is well displayed: in the coarse-grained graded part of the bed, cleavage is almost at 90° to bedding, but in the fine-grained top the angle is reduced to 30 or 40°.

The path leads uphill into the wood. To the south a number of blocky lichen-covered exposures of thickly bedded greywacke show 10 cm-long clasts in the top of graded beds, overlain by a finer grained laminated division.

Beyond the wood the valley widens, and is approximately parallel to the strike of the westward-dipping beds. Across the stream [6500 3055] the path is paved with large cleavage slabs of greywacke, which display a variety of sedimentary features typical of turbidites.

Locality 2 [6493 3071]   In these coarse-grained greywackes a crude stratification can be seen in places (interval *b*), but a few beds also show large-scale cross-stratification, which is unusual in turbidites.

Locality 3 Rising uphill, the path crosses a 2 to 3 m-thick unit of greenish grey siltstone and mudstone within the thickly-bedded greywacke near a wall in heather-covered ground [6524 3030]. Some parts show parallel- and cross-lamination on the weathered surface. There are some thin graded greywacke beds, 7 to 20 cm thick, which include intervals *a, b, c* and *d*.

Locality 4 Uphill the path passes into the 'National Nature Reserve' and at this point some of the bedding planes exposed in the path show good ice-carved grooves; linear, parallel-sided scratches trending just south of east, and quite distinct from lineations caused by joints or cleavage. They are well displayed in a small area about 70 m NW of the cairn.

From the top of the col one may return to Cwm Bychan via Llyn Morwynion [658 303], a small lake in a deep basin carved along one of the NW-trending lineaments which cross the Rhinogs. The more determined walker may follow the footpath which encircles Rhinog Fawr. The path is marked on the Dolgellau 1:50 000 topographic sheet (124). It begins from the col of Bwlch Tyddiad and runs downhill into the forest. Turn south on to the forestry road, cross the Afon Crawcwellt and follow it for 200 m. Bear west along the second fire break and leave the forest. The path leads southwest into the col, following the edge of the boulder clay. Bwlch Drws Ardudwy is lower than Bwlch Tyddiad, but crosses a similar sequence of thickly bedded greywackes between scree-covered slopes of Rhinog Fawr to the north and Rhinog Fach to the south. Where the valley widens, a marsh area marks the site of a former lake. To the south-west the river has cut a marked V-shaped trench in the floor of the glaciated U-shaped valley. On some of the rock pavements formed by the dip slopes of the greywackes, ice-scoured grooves are clearly visible. The well marked path descends to the road in Cwm Nantcol near Maes-y-garnedd. From here take the footpath to the north, past Nantcol cottage. As the path rises it crosses the top of the Rhinog Formation on to the softer-weathering shales of the Hafotty Formation, and on the hilltop passes on to boulder clay which shows sorted stone stripes on the surface. The footpath crosses the wall and follows the gully downhill to Gloyw Lyn and then to Cwm Bychan.

A third possible route to follow from Bwlch Tyddiad is to continue eastwards through the forest and take one of the various routes to the Trawsfynydd–Dolgellau road (A470). The old route through the forest probably followed the Afon Crawcwellt, but now it is easier to follow the forestry road, turning left when joining it.

12 Drovers' Road, Llanbedr to Bontddu

This is one of the most picturesque walks in North Wales (Figure 30). It follows the old route from Llanbedr to Bontddu, via Pont Scethin, which Fay Godwin and Shirley Toulson described in their book *The Drovers' roads of Wales*. It is possible to take a train from Barmouth to Llanbedr Halt for the start of the walk, and to catch the Crosville bus back from Bontddu to Barmouth at the end. Alternatively a path leads westwards from the Hirgwm valley [650 202] through Bwlch y Rhiwgyr to Tal-y-bont about 4 km S of Llanbedr.

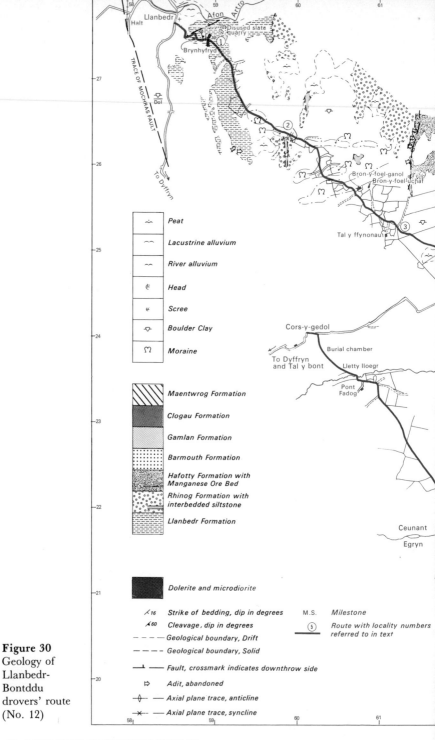

Figure 30
Geology of Llanbedr-Bontddu drovers' route (No. 12)

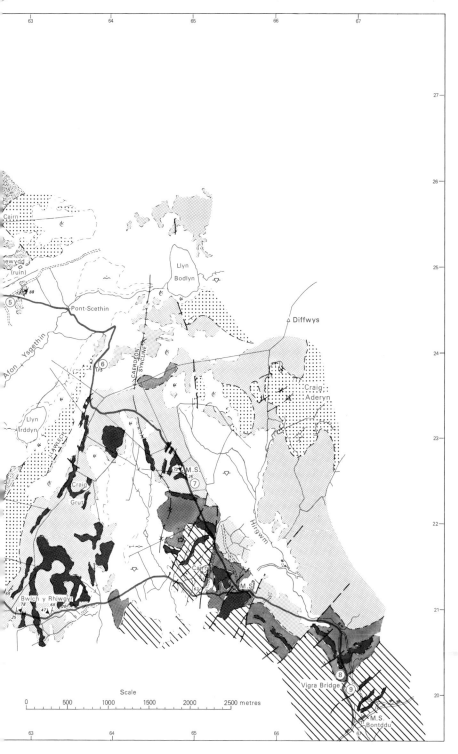

The Llanbedr to Bontddu route is approximately 15 km; the circular route via Bwlch y Rhiwgyr is about 25 km. Both involve a stiff climb over the Rhinogs. All the formations of the Harlech Grits Group, except the Dolwen Formation, are crossed on these walks, which clearly indicate the influence of geology on scenery.

South of the bridge over Afon Artro in Llanbedr follow the first road on the left by Capel Moriah. Take the right fork which climbs steeply uphill and past Brynhyfryd cottage.

Locality 1   The Llanbedr Formation is exposed in the woods to the west and along the roadside. It consists of medium to greyish green cleaved siltstone with well-developed, closely-spaced cleavage which makes this horizon suitable for roofing slate. The slate has been worked near Llanbedr, Llanfair and in a number of other places. Small kink bands which deform the cleavage indicate a second period of deformation. There are several thin intrusions of dolerite within the slates, e.g. near a wall [5890 2651] on the north side of the road where the dolerite forms a massive lichen-covered crag.

Uphill, the walls change gradually from being composed of slabs of Llanbedr slate to more uneven blocks of greywacke derived mainly from the Rhinog Formation.

To the west of the woods there is a fine panoramic view towards the Rhinogs, and further uphill the conical peak of Moelfre comes into view. The road here lies roughly parallel to the strike of the rocks.

The change in land use from woodland and scrub to numerous small walled fields marks the change from solid rock to boulder clay. Erratics, some of them very large, are scattered on the surface.

Locality 2 [5990 2535]   Slightly off the track to the south, adjacent to a footpath, thickly bedded medium- to coarse-grained greywacke of the Rhinog Formation is exposed. These rocks are resistant to weathering and stand out in prominent crags above the level of the boulder clay.

From this point the steep northern slope of a lateral moraine is well displayed to the south-east. It is a linear feature, and is part of the moraine complex which separated the glaciers of the Dwyryd valley to the north from the Ysgethin valley to the south. To the south two more moraine ridges are apparent, but westwards they become less distinct and merge into the surrounding boulder clay. To the north-west from the top of the moraine one can see across Tremadoc Bay to the Lleyn Peninsula and, if there is low tide, the seaward extension of this moraine, Sarn Badrig, is visible. The well-marked sand dunes, which die out towards Mochras Island and the Artro estuary, define the edge of Morfa Dyffryn. Mochras Island is a low boulder clay ridge separated from the spread of boulder clay by estuarine sands, silts and wind-blown sand. This spit was the site of the

Mochras Borehole, which proved a thick sequence of Tertiary, Jurassic and Triassic sediments, and thus initiated an entirely new interpretation of the geology of the Irish Sea, and changed markedly the palaeogeographical interpretation of the Mesozoic Era on land.

To the east, Moelfre, which stands out as an isolated peak, is capped by shales of the Hafotty Formation, which rest on greywackes of the Rhinog Formation. The hill is covered with blocky debris produced by freeze-thaw action and *in situ* rock exposure is relatively sparse. Towards the lower slopes of the hill the position of the Moelfre Fault, a N–S-trending reverse fault, is marked only by a slight change in slope. This fault downthrows to the west, and the succession of Hafotty Formation resting on the Rhinog Formation is repeated. About 500 m NE of Bron-y-foel-uchaf Farm the manganese ore-bed near the base of the Hafotty Formation, which also occurs high on Moelfre, has been worked. The old workings and tips, marked by a line of bushes, stop southwards at the edge of thick boulder clay.

Pass through the gate, cross the 'main' road signed for Nantcol and take the road straight ahead marked as a 'cul-de-sac'. To the south-east this road crosses two bracken-covered morainic ridges before passing on to the thick spread of boulder clay which fills the Ysgethin valley. Where the road forks at Bron-y-foel-ganol Farm take the right branch which winds its way uphill. Beyond the track leading off to Tal y ffynonau the road deteriorates into a grass-covered mountain path.

Locality 3 [6122 2433] From here it is possible to see along the Glaslyn valley to Snowdon, and to the west Moel Hebog, Mynydd Craig Goch and Yr Effel on the Lleyn Peninsula. Also the estuarine flats of Morfa Harlech and Traeth Bach, south of Portmadoc are visible, as well as Morfa Dyffryn and Cardigan Bay.

To the south-east, the path crosses the line of the Moelfre Fault and blocks of white quartz, possibly from a vein along the fault, are scattered on the slopes above.

Locality 4 In the Ysgethin valley the long ridge in front stretches up to Diffwys. This locality provides a good viewpoint to observe the geology and its effect on the scenery. The eastward dipping succession lies on the western limb of the Caerdeon syncline. The Rhinog Formation is concealed under boulder clay on the lower slopes, but is exposed on Craig y Dinas which lies to the south of the path. The lower hill to the south of the main ridge is in the Hafotty Formation, and to the south-east the craggier ground is formed by greywackes of the Barmouth Formation. The ridge is capped by the silty shales of the Gamlan Formation. The junction of the Barmouth and Gamlan formations can be picked out, rising uphill with the shales of the Gamlan Formation on the grassy slopes to the east. These formations are partially covered by scree and head. A fault associated with the axis of the Caerdeon syncline passes through Llyn Bodlyn. The fault, which trends N–S, coincides with the western margin of the lake and downthrows to the west. The steep crags south of the lake consist of greywacke of the Barmouth Formation. Boulder clay, which floors the valley, forms a natural dam for Llyn Bodlyn, though the level has been raised artificially. Llyn Dulyn and other small ice-carved rock basins mark the retreat of the Ysgethin glacier up the valley in the waning stages of the glaciation. Llyn Irddyn is another glacial lake, in this case dammed by a lateral moraine.

From here the path passes into open moorland and becomes difficult to identify. A small cairn marks the next fork. The north-eastern fork leads to the head of the valley and to the ruins of the old coaching inn, Tynewydd, which is visible to the east of the plot of conifers. The route follows the south-eastern fork downhill to Pont-Scethin (Figure 31), a fine example of functional rural architecture, and then zig-zags past the Janet Haigh memorial stone up the ridge on the other side of the valley where it follows the outcrop of the softer Gamlan Flags.

Locality 5 [6285 2372]   At this exposure are banded, grey siltstones typical of the Hafotty Formation, with bands of parallel- and cross-lamination, 2 to 3 cm thick, alternating with featureless grey siltstone.

Downhill the lower slopes of peat-covered boulder clay support a prolific covering of sedges. The boulder clay is exposed on a meander scar just downstream from Pont-Scethin.

Locality 6 [about 6380 2286]   A few poor exposures of cleaved, grey, banded siltstone of the Gamlan Formation occur near the summit.

To the north the Rhinog, Hafotty, Barmouth and Gamlan formations can be identified on the Moelfre/Y Llethr ridge, and there is a marked contrast between the lower gentle, boulder clay-covered slopes and the drift-free, craggy ground above. In general, the areas of boulder clay have been enclosed by stone walls, and form better farm land than the rocky open slopes used entirely as sheep pasture. High on this hillside scattered erratics of dolerite and greywacke prove that the entire ridge was overridden by the ice-sheet during glaciation. Subsequently periglacial mass wasting produced rounded hilltops and altiplanation terraces.

The walls crossing the summit are composed almost entirely of blocks of siltstone derived from the Gamlan Formation. From the summit the footpath contours the hill to the

Figure 31
Sketch of
Pont Scethin

east before descending into the valley. It is cut into a thick cover of soliflucted drift, the only exposures of solid being in small slip scars.

Downhill the path follows the Gamlan Formation along the eastern side of a spur above the Hirgwm valley. On the eastern side of the valley the coarse greywackes of the underlying Barmouth Formation crop out in a number of open folds. From north to south the axes of an anticline, a syncline and an anticline can be detected. South of Craig Aderyn the beds dip away to the south.

Locality 7 [6487 2158] To the west of the path, cleaved banded siltstones of the Gamlan Formation are exposed, but altered dolerite intruding the siltstones stands out as more blocky exposures. Cleavage in the dolerite forms open fractures in contrast to the slaty cleavage developed in the adjacent siltstones.

Downhill, exposure is poor. From near the large erratic [6521 2087] of coarse greywacke, a fault-line scarp stands above the path to the west. This is the extension of the fault that bounds Llyn Bodlyn. Here, interbedded silty mudstone and coarse quartzose siltstone of the Maentwrog Formation are thrown down against the black shales of the Clogau Formation. Farther downhill, black mudstone near the base of the Clogau Formation crops out on the path [6522 2074].

The path meets the road at the Tal-y-bont milestone [6558 2025]. At this point one has the choice of following the path west to Tal-y-bont or the metalled road to Bontddu.

Tal-y-bont The path west follows the old route across the Sylfaen valley, crossing the Llawlech ridge at the spectacular Bwlch y Rhiwgyr and hence to Pont-Fadog on Afon

Ysgethin; the route again traverses the succession from the Maentwrog to the Rhinog Formation.

The Barmouth Formation is exposed adjacent to the path on the north side of the Bwlch. The thickly bedded, coarse-grained greywacke shows typical turbidite features. From Pont-Fadog a metalled road to Cors-y-Gedol passing a burial chamber (Figure 32) [603 228] joins the main road (A496) just north of Tal-y-bont.

Figure 32   Sketch of burial chamber near Tal-y-bont

Bontddu   Follow the metalled road down the Hirgwm valley to the telephone box near Pont Hirgwm [6673 1977]. Here take the footpath which follows the river down to Bontddu. The workings of the Clogau mine can be seen on the hill to the east. Near the gate the footpath crosses the remains of an old leat which took water from the river near the bridge to drive the West Clogau mill, probably built in about 1862. Only the terraced dressing floors of the mill remain among the trees where the path draws near the river [6676 1960]. About 70 m farther on, new tips and machinery outside the Llechfraith adit reflect recent work to re-open the Clogau workings. Indeed, a substantial gold find from here was reported in 1980.

Locality 8   A small outcrop of very dark grey pyritic mudstone partly covered by head is typical of the Clogau Formation, the basal division of the Mawddach Group. Gold miners in the 19th century discovered that the most productive part of any vein occurred where it intersected this formation (see Excursion 3). About 150 m farther, some beds of black micaceous sandstone up to 30 cm thick, uncommon in this formation, crop out within the mudstone [6683 1922].

Locality 9   At Vigra Bridge the path crosses the river and the contact between the Clogau and Maentwrog formations. The river runs roughly normal to strike here, crossing a thick succession of thinly interbedded silty mudstone and coarser quartzose siltstone of the Maentwrog Formation. The coarse siltstone beds diminish in frequency upwards, and at the end of the path, in Bontddu, they are uncommon. Numerous sills of dolerite and intermediate rocks are exposed in the river section (see Excursion 3).

On the west of the river at Vigra Bridge are the ruins of the old Vigra Mill which was probably built in the 1840s to process ore from the Vigra copper mine. The mine, situated on the hillside above the mill about 400 m to the west, was possibly worked for copper in the 18th century or earlier. It was most productive from 1825 to 1845. From 1854, when gold was discovered in the St David's Lode, to 1911, the mill at Vigra Bridge was used mainly by the Clogau mine.

13   New Precipice Walk

This well-made path high above the Mawddach estuary follows a tramway which served the gold mines on Foel Ispri. Even though it remains mostly within the Maentwrog Formation there is much of geological interest along it. Access to the walk is by a minor road north of the main road (A496) opposite the Penmaenpool toll bridge. Some visitors leave their cars at the first fork (Figure 33) in the road, where the Nant Cesailgwm joins Afon Cwm-Mynach [690 200]; others follow the right fork through the gate and park near Nant Cesailgwm [696 205]. Most drive to Foel Ispri uchaf where the footpath starts. The path more or less follows the 260 m contour. The usual walk ends near the mine workings at the edge of

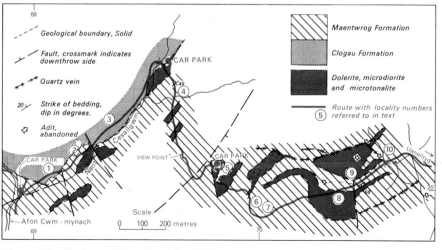

Figure 33   Geology of New Precipice Walk (No. 13)

the forest about 1 km from Foel Ispri uchaf, but it is very pleasant to continue on to Llanelltyd, a distance of about 2.5 km from the farm.

Locality 1   The road here cuts through the southern side of a tree-covered hillock which is composed of sandy cobbly gravel overlain by about 1 m of brown boulder clay with sandy lenses near the bottom. The gravel was deposited by a stream which flowed under the Devensian ice-sheet before the boulder clay was deposited during deglaciation.

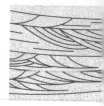

Cross bedding

Locality 2   Along the road there are several outcrops of thinly interbedded cleaved, grey silty mudstone and fine quartzose sandstone of the Maentwrog Formation (p. 55). These sedimentary rocks dip roughly south-east and are intruded by thin sills of grey altered microtonalite.

Locality 3   Black and dark grey mudstone of the underlying Clogau Formation is exposed here. The mudstone is banded, cleaved and contains plentiful pyrite, including some 1 cm cubes. The mudstone is folded in several small anticlines and synclines, and the cleavage is parallel to the axial planes. Intrusions similar to those in the overlying formation are also present.

At the second parking place the road bends sharply, and amongst the oak trees there are many outcrops of moderately to steeply dipping silty mudstone and fine sandstone of the lower Maentwrog Formation intruded by thin sills. At *Locality 4* the characteristic sedimentary structures of the formation can be examined (p. 23).

Beyond the forest the road climbs to the farm. About 200 m below the farm [6966 2013] is a good viewpoint situated just on the east side of the axis of the Dolwen pericline. To the north, the bedding on Diffwys can be seen dipping west while on Y Garn it dips east. There are splendid views down the Mawddach estuary.

Locality 5   In the car park at the start of New Precipice Walk, a thin sliver of sedimentary rocks and a quartz vein can be seen between two sills. The upper sill is green dolerite which is exposed at several places at the start of the walk.

Locality 6   From here the track lies approximately along the strike of the Maentwrog Formation which, with the sills within it, is well exposed in craggy outcrops. Parallel- and cross-lamination, lens-like beds and separated ripples may be seen in the sandstone beds.

Locality 7   Here, and farther along the path, the rocks are folded. Minor crenulations occur between well-developed fractures, several centimetres apart, which lie parallel to the axial planes of the folds.

Locality 8   The path here crosses the foot of a tip outside an old lead/zinc mine working. Over the next 500 m there are many adits both above and below the path. These workings lie along quartz veins, trending roughly E–W, which contain mainly sphalerite and galena with lesser amounts of other sulphide minerals. Most of the workings were opened after 1888, though the veins are thought to have been worked in ancient times. Up to 1900, when they were consolidated under the name Voel Mines, several companies worked this vein system for lead, zinc and gold. The workings are extensive, but total production was very small and a great deal of investment money was lost.

Locality 9 Beyond the well near the last locality the path forks. The lower path is the correct one to follow but, a little to the east of the point where the upper path crosses an old incline, there is an interesting small outcrop of baked silty mudstone in contact with an underlying dolerite sill.

Locality 10 The lower path leads along a wall to a wooden footbridge above which there are several thick quartz veins within the sedimentary rocks. There is a filled-in adit above the veins, and in the associated tip there is plenty of sphalerite.

The path continues from the footbridge to a stile over a wall into the forest [7070 2013] and can be followed down to Llanelltyd.

14 Precipice Walk

Precipice Walk (Figure 34) is a courtesy footpath around Foel Cynwch on land owned by the Nannau Estate. There is a car park and W.C. at the junction of two minor roads [7458 2113]. The round trip from the car park is about 5.5 km. The walk itself is approximately along the 240 m contour. Precipice Walk is signposted from Dolgellau.

Most visitors follow the walk anticlockwise around the mountain. It traverses well exposed rocks of the Ffestiniog Flags Formation, and various intrusions.

Locality 1 Thinly interbedded light grey silty mudstone and white, coarse quartzose siltstone of the Ffestiniog Flags Formation are gently folded into an anticline and faulted. The siltstone, in beds up to 12 cm thick, locally reach 25 cm in channel-fills and show lens-like bedding, parallel- and ripple-lamination. The silty mudstone is cleaved. At the northern end of the exposure there is a small lens-shaped area, 60 × 45 cm, of breccia. All the fragments are of rocks from the Ffestiniog Flags Formation. Such breccias form thin dykes and sills, and are common on this mountain. They are intrusive breccias emplaced during the Rhobell Volcanic Group magmatic episode.

Locality 2 A crag near where two walls converge is composed of grey porphyritic microtonalite. Numerous concordant intrusions of microdiorite and microtonalite are com-

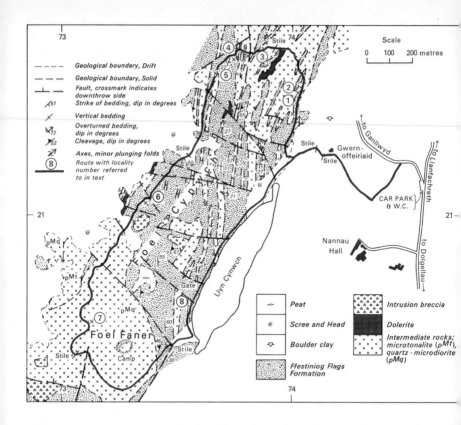

Figure 34
Geology of Precipice
Walk (No. 14)

mon all over Foel Cynwch and are well exposed on the
northern part of this walk. They represent the south-western
extension of the subvolcanic intrusion complex at Moel
Llan (see Excursion 4), emplaced beneath the Rhobell Faw
volcano. On the eastern side of Llyn Cynwch there is a sharp
increase in the number of intrusions, and on the lower slope
of Foel Offrwm, which is an outlier of Ordovician volcanic
rocks, eruptive rocks of the Rhobell episode are also exposed.
Prior to the eruption of the Rhobell lavas the underlying
sedimentary rocks were tilted eastwards and folded, hence
the marked unconformity beneath the lavas. Subsequent
folding during the Caledonian earth movements steepened
this initial tilt and modified the folds. Thus, though in most
exposures round this path the bedding dips at only moderate
angles eastwards, elsewhere on the mountain, particularly
where there is a dense complex of intrusions, the bedding
may be vertical or overturned.

Locality 3   Alongside the foundations of a small building is
an erratic, 1.5 m long, of lapilli tuff derived from the lower
Ordovician volcanic succession.

Locality 4   In this area there are many outcrops in which the
sedimentary structures in the Ffestiniog Flags Formation are

Figure 35 Ffestiniog Flags Formation intruded by a thin sill of microtonalite

well displayed on weathered surfaces (Figure 35). Note especially the collapsed ripples, with flat tops and lobate bases, and the layers of totally disrupted sandstone beds between perfectly flat, uniform beds. Note also the lineations on bedding planes caused by cleavage/bedding intersections.

Locality 5 Outcrops of microdiorite contain xenoliths of country rock and abundant 1 cm pyrite cubes.

Locality 6 The bedding here is totally disrupted. These outcrops are on the northern edge of a large breccia pipe which forms the prominent rocky knoll. There are four similar pipes on Foel Cynwch all intruded during the episode of Rhobell volcanism. In porphyry copper districts such bodies are commonly mineralised and, indeed, a pipe at Glasdir, a little over 1 km to the north-west, was mined for copper until 1914.

The view of the Mawddach valley from this locality is informative: the river meanders along the flat-bottomed valley, and dry channels and old cut-off meanders are visible. The lower slopes on both sides of the valley are scree-covered.

Locality 7 Outcrops by the fence along the path are of a

large, faulted quartz-microdiorite intrusion complex. It is possibly laccolithic and one of several similar intrusions on the eastern side of the Harlech dome. The rock contains spots of epidote, some with pyritic centres, which probably represent infilled vesicles.

Locality 8 Despite the wall at the southern end, Llyn Cynwch, now used as a reservoir, is a natural lake occupying a depression in a subglacial channel. Outflow at both ends of the lake is blocked by boulder clay. Note that the bedding in the outcrops hereabouts is nearly vertical.

15 Ty'n-y-groes to Gwynfynydd

The walk starts (Figure 36) from the Forestry Commission car park [7300 2341] on the banks of the Mawddach opposite the Ty'n-y-groes hotel, which is on the main A470 Dolgellau–Trawsfynydd road. This popular, easy walk is used by tourists visiting the Gwynfynydd gold mine. It follows Forestry Commission roads mostly through mature forest along the Afon Mawddach for about 4.5 km to the gold mine.

Locality 1 Looking westwards through the trees, the terraces on the opposite bank of the river are clearly visible. In late glacial or immediate post-glacial times, outwash carried down the Mawddach valley from the retreating glaciers blocked the valley at least down to its confluence with the Lâs and Wen valleys. Subsequently the blockage was breached and the terraces, five in all, have formed as the Mawddach gradually cut down to its present base level.

On the banks of the Mawddach about 100 m N of *Locality 1* are outcrops of grey slaty beds of the Maentwrog Formation. The cleavage is practically coincident with the bedding, and it is possible to collect *Olenus gibbosus, Glyptagnostus reticulatus* and *Homagnostus obesus*, which indicate the *Olenus* Zone of the Merioneth Series.

Locality 2 The cutting here, a little north of a small stream, exposes about 6 m of the uppermost terrace. It is composed of poorly sorted and stratified cobbly gravels in a sandy silt matrix. In places the gravels have a hard ferruginous cement. Soliflucted clay with abundant shale fragments overlies the uppermost silty gravel.

Locality 3 About 200 m SW of the footbridge, light grey, banded silty mudstone with laminae and beds up to 12 cm thick of white, quartzose fine sandstone of the Maentwrog Formation are exposed. A sill, just over a metre thick, of grey feldspar-porphyry shows perfectly concordant and sharp contacts. There are numerous exposures in road cuttings, and in the river bed north of here and at the footbridge gentle undulations in the bedding are clearly seen.

Locality 4 Just beyond the road fork a small anticline is exposed in a culvert on the low road. Such minor folds are

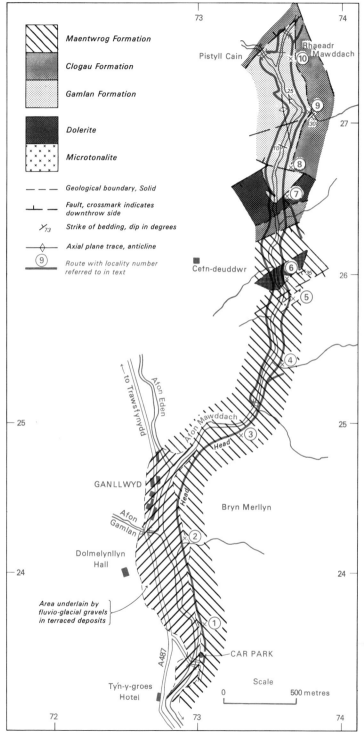

Figure 36 Ty'n-y-groes to Gwyn-fynydd (No. 15)

common, but major folds, which disturb the regional north–south strike and the overall eastward dip, are uncommon. The rocks, with mudstone beds up to 15 cm thick, are typical of the lower part of the Maentwrog Formation.

Locality 5   Grey microtonalite, which is pyritic and locally altered, is exposed.

Locality 6   A partly filled trial level on the eastern side of the road is one of many in the area. The trial, probably for gold, followed a quartz-vein in dolerite. This area, however, is within the pyrite-rich zone surrounding the Coed-y-Brenin porphyry copper deposit (Excursion 4), and the green and blue secondary copper minerals staining the walls of the excavation show that the rock contains chalcopyrite in addition to pyrite.

Locality 7   Green dolerite is exposed just past a turn-off to the right which leads to the Turf mine and the porphyry copper deposit at Capel Hermon.

Locality 8   The exposure, due east of the old Tyddyn Gwladys gold mine, is in rocks transitional between the Gamlan and Clogau formations. Compact, grey banded siltstone, with beds of fine quartzose sandstone up to 60 cm thick, overlies 60 cm of black mudstone, which in turn overlies dark grey mudstone with thin beds of quartzose siltstone and pyrite laminae. The underlying Gamlan Formation is exposed in the river. At the southern end of the exposure a dolerite dyke, 2 m thick, intrudes the sedimentary rocks. All the rock types at this locality include much pyrite, both disseminated and in veinlets, some of which also contain chalcopyrite.

Locality 9   The large road cutting, opposite an old, overgrown stone building, is in rocks of the Gamlan Formation. Mostly it consists of grey siltstone with thin sandstone beds and laminae of pinkish manganiferous rock composed of spessartine and quartz. The outcrop is crossed by a low-angle fault. The fault plane shows slickensides and black manganese staining. A few metres beyond the small stream a steep normal fault is exposed. The strata on the downthrow side, which contain a thin sill, are more broken than on the upthrow side. All the rocks are heavily stained with iron and manganese minerals.

Locality 10   The waterfalls Rhaiadr Mawddach and the top of Pistyll Cain as well as part of the ruins of the Gwynfynyd Mill can be viewed from here. A hundred metres beyond this locality a track on the left leads downhill to Pont Gilrhyd. Here, turn south to visit the mill ruins or north to visit the mine. Details of the privately owned mine area are given in the next walk (No. 16).

A pleasant alternative walk back to the car park is along

the west bank of the river. Cross Pont Gilrhyd, then follow
the path through the mill ruins to cross the bridge over the
Afon Gain below Pistyll Cain. From there follow the track
southwards, by-passing Ferndale by taking the short footpath on to the forestry road about 150 m S of the mill ruins.
The track leads to a footbridge across the Mawddach near
Locality 3.

16   Pont Dolgefeiliau to Gwynfynydd

The area of the Coed-y-Brenin forest between the Afon Eden and
Afon Mawddach has been developed by the Forestry Commission
for recreation and, starting at the Forestry Commission car park
near the A470, Dolgellau–Trawsfynydd road at Dolgefeiliau
[7225 2686], there are numerous footpaths, all marked on the
Forestry Commission maps which can be obtained from the Forest
Visitor Centre at Maesgwm, 3 km N of Ganllwyd. There are many
points of geological interest on these paths, some of which are given
below. The route presented defines a circular tour of about 10 km of
moderate to easy walking but the map (Figure 37) can be used in
conjunction with the Forestry Commission footpath map, and the
outcrops described visited by almost any combination of the forest
paths. Gwynfynydd gold mine is currently being worked and
visitors to it should remain strictly on the public footpaths.

From Pont Dolgefeiliau the footpath strikes south eastwards,
across the boulder-strewn hillside. Sections in drainage
ditches reveal only boulder clay, which overlies the Hafotty
and Barmouth formations. At the edge of the meadow
around Cefndeuddwr the path bears north to the forest road.

Locality 1   The section exposed in the road cutting is typical
of the Gamlan Formation consisting of grey siltstone, either
massive or laminated, with 1-cm thick chloritic beds and
greywacke beds 1 to 10 cm thick. Towards the top of the section thick beds of coarse-grained, quartzose sandstone occur.
The turbiditic character of these beds is clearly demonstrable
in the sedimentary structures they contain which can be examined in the loose blocks. Pyrite is locally abundant.

Locality 2   Thick beds of coarse-grained quartzose sand-
stone, pebbly at the bases, contain grains of blue quartz.
Such quartz is common in the sandstones of the Harlech
Grits Group.

Locality 3   On the west of the road there is an old gold working or trial level which followed a vein along a fault. Near the
road the open stope is filled with rubbish, and below it the
entrance is blocked. The waste tips are partly overgrown,
but quartz, calcite, a little pyrite, rare chalcopyrite, galena
and sphalerite can all be found. Most of the rock waste is of
the Gamlan Formation, but some black mudstone is of the
overlying Clogau Formation. Indeed, these mudstones are
exposed in the cutting above the old level at the junction with
the R576 and they contain bands, disseminations and

imple grading

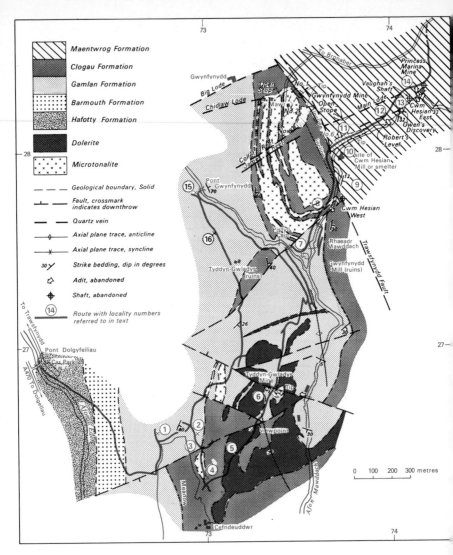

Figure 37 Pont Dolgefeiliau to Gwynfynydd (No. 16)

veinlets of pyrite and pyrrhotite (which is magnetic). The mudstone is well bedded, but broken into blocks by closely spaced joint sets. At the crossroads a large block of quartz shows most of the characteristics of the gold-bearing quartz veins: anastomosing sets of minor veins, enclosed blocks of wall rock, stringers rich in sulphides including pyrite, sphalerite, chalcopyrite and bornite.

Locality 4 A small outcrop of pyrite-rich microtonalite, near the junction of the R57 and R572, is typical of the minor sills in the region.

Locality 5 An exposure on the R572 contains the junction between intrusions of grey microtonalite and dolerite. The locality is at the edge of a thick dolerite sill.

The Forestry road (R572) ends about 200 m beyond *Locality 5* although a footpath continues. Close to its begining a wooden bench is sited at a viewpoint overlooking the Mawddach valley. The rusty, treeless scar on the east side of the valley is intensely pyritised microtonalite within the pyrite zone around the Coed-y-Brenin porphyry copper deposit (see Excursion 3).

Locality 6 The path crosses the lower part of a tip outside one of the upper levels of the old Tyddyn Gwladys gold mine. The vein that was worked is 1 m thick and dips about 70° N. The tip is composed mostly of crushed rock, all the vein material having been taken to lower levels.

The footpath winds downhill to join a forest road by the Afon Mawddach. Turn south at the road, follow it for 50 m, then turn east down a path to the lower road which leads to the bridge over the river below Pistyll Cain and thence to Gwynfynydd gold mine.

There were several mines in this small area and detailed accounts of their history are given in *The Gold Mines of Merioneth* by G. W. Hall and *Goldmining in Western Merioneth* by T. A. Morrison. Roughly one-third of all the gold produced in Merioneth came from Gwynfynydd. Mining at Gwynfynydd ceased in 1935 when the mill burned down, but periodical attempts at revival are still made as at present. For a person interested in mining archaeology there is much to see in this area.

Locality 7 A mill was built here in the early 1890s. Water was taken by a leat from the top of the Rhaiadr Mawddach, and by pipeline from above Pistyll Cain to a concrete storage tank from which it passed down a steel pipe to drive turbines. Only the mill foundations are now visible.

The track northwards from the mill site to the old workings was originally a tramway, but is now a public footpath. The rocks exposed in the river bed up to, and a little beyond, Pont Gilrhyd are of the Gamlan Formation, though the waterfall, Rhaiadr Mawddach, is over a microtonalite sill.

Locality 8 Cwm Hesian West mine, visible through the trees on the east bank was worked for lead in the early 1840s. Gold was found here, but it was difficult to separate from the associated sulphides and little work was done after 1864. The outcrop in the river is very dark grey, banded silty mudstone of the Clogau Formation.

Locality 9 Here the Trawsfynydd fault crosses the river. The Maentwrog Formation on the east is thrown down against the Clogau Formation containing a dolerite sill. The throw on this major fault increases northwards, and near Trawsfynydd the Clogau Formation is thrown against the Rhinog Formation. In the Gwynfynydd mine the fault divides two major vein systems, and correlation across it has always presented a tantalising problem.

Locality 10 The ruins of the Cwm Hesian mill are on the east bank. The outcrops in the river bed clearly display the characteristics of the interbedded silty mudstone, coarse quartzose siltstone and fine sandstone of the Maentwrog Formation (p. 24).

Locality 11: No 6 adit of Gwynfynydd gold mine. The mines in this area worked ENE-trending quartz veins containing galena, sphalerite, minor pyrite and rare chalcopyrite in association with the gold. This assemblage contrasts sharply with the chalcopyrite-dominant assemblage in the veins mined at the Clogau gold mine (Excursion 3). Of all the veins here, the Chidlaw was the most productive on the west of the Trawsfynydd fault; the Main, which may be an upward extension of it, was the most productive on the east.

The path crosses old waste tips for about 200 m before passing on to open hillside.

Locality 12: Robert's Level. A sill of microtonalite with good columnar jointing intrudes the Maentwrog Formation and forms the waterfall.

Locality 13 The thick quartz vein here is named Owen's Discovery. It is rich in sulphide minerals, including pyrite, sphalerite, galena and chalcopyrite. It trends ENE, and across the river was mined at Cwm Hesian East, said to be the first mine in the area to yield gold in 1844.

Locality 14 Just above the river the path passes the flooded Vaughan Shaft. Adits, shafts and tips hereabouts are part of the Bedd-y-Coedwr or Princess Marina mine, named because the gold for the princess' wedding ring came from here.

The path continues up the hill and joins the road from Bronaber to the Bedd-y-Coedwr farm. For those walkers who have an aversion to retracing their steps, follow the Bronaber road westwards for about 1.5 km, then turn south down the track to Gwynfynydd Farm. The footpath passes the farm and joins a forest road which leads to Pont Gwynfynydd. Whatever return is chosen it is worth visiting Pont Gwynfynydd and *Localities 15* and *16*.

Locality 15 Near the cross-roads west of the bridge there is an excellent exposure of steeply dipping beds of coarse-grained quartzose sandstone of the Gamlan Formation. The beds, up to 1 m thick, are graded with pebbly bases, laminated fine-grained tops, and are typical of the turbidites in this formation. The sandstones are cross-cut by thin quartz veins, one of which is rich in galena. These veins are the westward extension of part of the vein system worked in Gwynfynydd gold mine. This excellent exposure continues in the river, below the bridge.

Locality 16 At this locality the manganiferous rocks of the Gamlan Formation are well exposed. Pale pinkish yellow bands, nodules and lenses rarely more than 1 cm thick in grey or purplish grey siltstone are composed mainly of spessartine. The origin of the manganese is uncertain: it has been suggested that it was deposited in special conditions as rhodochrosite, the carbonate, as a gel on the seafloor and was metamorphosed to spessartine. In this outcrop the manganese bands have a black weathered surface of manganese oxides. The irregular bedding planes are the result of the original gelatinous layer being compressed between silt layers.

Most outcrops along the road from here are in the Gamlan Formation. There is a particularly good outcrop about 400 m S [7317 2728]. A few metres beyond it a footpath crosses the road. This path can be followed south-westwards to near *Locality 2*, and then any of the routes shown on the Forestry Commission map can be followed back to the car park.

17 Torrent Walk

This delightful, short walk along the Afon Clywedog starts near the bridge over the river [7523 1880] on a minor road linking the A470 and A494 via Dolserau. The path (Figure 38) follows the river upstream and ends on the B4416 road to Brithdir [7612 1805].

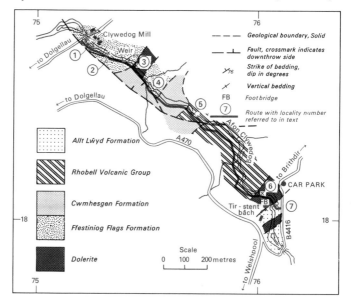

Figure 38 Geology of Torrent Walk (No. 17)

Parking is easier at the end of the walk, but geologically it is more instructive to start near the bridge. There is an excellently exposed section through two of the upper Cambrian formations, the Rhobell Volcanic Group and the overlying Aran Volcanic Group. However, it is hazardous to attempt to enter any of the gorges, and this walk should not be used as a substitute for the Capel Hermon excursion (No. 4).

Locality 1   Under the bridge and a little upstream there are outcrops of light grey cleaved siltstone of the Ffestiniog Flags Formation. Throughout this formation thick units of siltstone beds alternate with units of thinly interbedded fine quartzose sandstone or coarse siltstone and silty mudstone. Blocks from the latter unit have been used on the parapet of the bridge, and show the lens-like bedding, cross-lamination and inverted ripples typical of the formation. There is also a block of Rhobell Volcanic Group basalt containing large hornblende phenocrysts.

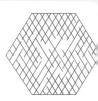

Typical basal section of amphibole crystal

Locality 2   Above the siltstone unit here, there are beds of quartzose sandstone up to 45 cm thick with thin alternations of very dark grey silty mudstone. The sandstone beds are mostly massive, but some show convoluted lamination. The beds are steeply dipping to vertical and they young to the south-east.

Locality 3   Dolerite is exposed in the stream near the steps in the path. This is in one of the two major sills within the Ffestiniog Flags Formation in this area. The basal contact can be seen in the north bank of the river.

Locality 4   Here, at a waterfall where a minor tributary joins the Clywedog and for 100 m or so upstream, the transitional nature of the junction between the Ffestiniog Flags and Cwmhesgen formations is clearly demonstrated. The bedding dips less steeply than downstream. The succession consists of units of medium grey mudstone interbedded with white coarse quartzose siltstone beds up to 2 cm thick alternating with very dark grey to black mudstone, characteristic of the overlying Cwmhesgen Formation.

Locality 5   The junction with the Cwmhesgen Formation is not visible, but mudstone of the lower Dolgellau Member is well exposed along the river. The mudstone is dark grey to black, cleaved, richly pyritic in parts and poorly bedded. Elsewhere (see Excursion 5) the mudstone is richly fossiliferous. It is separated from basaltic lavas of the Rhobell Volcanic Group at this locality by a thin intrusion of grey, pyritic, porphyritic quartz-microdiorite.

There are few outcrops on the path above this point, but exposure is continuous in the river, though dangerous to reach. Mostly the rock is greenish grey basaltic lava with phenocrysts of amphibole up to 1 cm long, feldspar and, in some varieties, pyroxene. There are some dolerite dykes.

Locality 6 Here, more accessible exposures in the river are of porphyritic dolerite intruded along the junction between the Rhobell Volcanic and Aran Volcanic groups.

Locality 7 The Allt Lŵyd Formation at the base of the Aran Volcanic Group is exposed below the bridge. On the south bank is grey amygdaloidal dolerite at the margin of an intrusion adjacent to a bed, 1 m thick, of coarse-grained feldspathic sandstone. On the north bank of the river coarse-grained feldspathic sandstone, with silty beds and lenses and pebbly bands up to 1 cm thick, is exposed. The pebbles are rounded, mostly igneous, and were derived from the underlying volcanic pile. Upwards the feldspathic sandstone becomes thinly interbedded with dark grey siltstone.

4 The Harlech dome road circuit

It is possible to examine eight of the formations that comprise the Harlech Grits and Mawddach groups, in addition to a number of other interesting features, at roadside localities around the Harlech dome. The complete circuit is about 65 km. It can be started at any point, but to do it more or less in stratigraphical order it is best to start at Harlech (Figure 39) and travel anticlockwise.

Locality 1 Harlech Castle [5808 3132]   Park at the Watergate entrance near the level crossing. The castle is built on a crag, which in historic times was a sea cliff, and the weathering of the rocks in the cliff is typical of a coastal outcrop. The castle is now separated from the sea by a broad flat of Recent sediments and sand dunes. The lower part of the exposure in the car park is in one of the rare silty horizons within the Rhinog Formation, here dipping at 30° ESE. The dark grey, cleaved silty mudstone contains thin beds of coarse-grained greywacke turbidites. The beds are graded, and the bases show moulds of scatch marks which are mostly load deformed. About 9 m from the base the thickly bedded, coarse-grained turbidites typical of the formation occur. The Rhinog Formation is also exposed in the cutting opposite Theatr Ardudwy.

Locality 2   The Llanbedr Formation is exposed in the disused slate quarry [5900 2670] south-east of Llanbedr. South from Llanbedr take the first turn left after Capel Moriah. The quarry is situated about 0.5 km to the east of the main road, and the waste tip lies to the north of the road. The formation consists of massive blue-grey mudstone with a closely-spaced, well-developed cleavage. There is little indication of bedding except on the western end of the quarry, where purplish grey mudstone and thin green sandy bands are interbedded. A thin dolerite sill, about 6 cm thick, crosses the quarry face and can be seen lensing out. Minor faults can also be seen.

The road south from Llanbedr skirts the edge of the Recent estuarine sediments, and the break in slope between these and the boulder clay, resting on Harlech Grits Group, roughly marks the line of the Mochras Fault. The exact throw of this fault is not known, but is in excess of 2000 m. A borehole drilled on Mochras (Shell) Island proved this thickness of Mesozoic and Tertiary sediments beneath the drift cover.

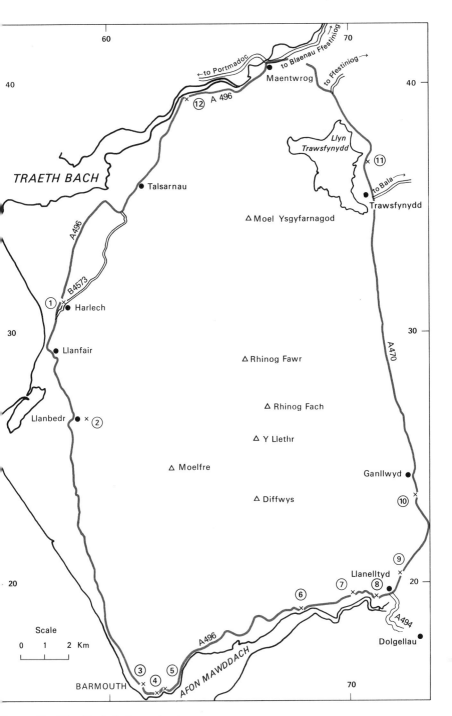

Figure 39 The Harlech dome circuit

Locality 3 St John's Church, Barmouth [6130 1595]
Between this locality and Aber Amffra Harbour on the
eastern side of town all formations from Hafotty to Maentwrog are exposed. At this locality the lower part of the Hafotty Formation, with the manganese ore-bed near the base, is
exposed. Full details of it are given under *Locality 1*, Excursion 2.

Locality 4 Porkington Terrace [6189 1560]   Park in the lay-
by opposite the houses, and from there visit the several exposures in the Barmouth and Gamlan formations in the
roadside, on the sea shore and near the bridge. At the
western end of the road cutting immediately west of Porkington Terrace, the junction between the Barmouth and
Gamlan formations is exposed. Two beds of coarse-grained
turbiditic sandstone separated by 53 cm of grey siltstone are
the uppermost beds of the Barmouth Formation. A minor
fault coincides with the top of the lower of the two beds. At
the base of the Gamlan Formation, 30 cm of fine sandstone
are overlain by light greenish grey, banded siltstone. Beds of
sandstone up to 60 cm thick are present at intervals above
this. Also in this cutting are two nearly vertical normal faults
throwing down to the east, one with a quartz vein along it.
   Many characteristics of the Gamlan Formation are
displayed on the weathered exposures along the beach below
this cutting. Thin beds of slumped sandstone (Figure 40) and
turbidites are interbedded with cleaved siltstone. The rocks
are folded, and both cleavage refractions and the fan-like
orientation of axial plane cleavage in a fold are well displayed

Figure 40
Slumped sandstone
bed in the Gamlan
Formation

Figure 41   Fold in the Gamlan Formation

(Figure 41). Near the railway bridge the siltstone is purple, and contains sparse green sandy beds with plentiful yellowish pink nodules as well as thin beds and laminae of spessartine rock.

Locality 5 Aber Amffra Harbour [6226 1574]   There is a parking area at the start of a picturesque footpath which leads up a wooded valley to Panorama Hill. On the western side of the valley and in adjacent road cuttings the black silty mudstone of the Clogau Formation, which conformably overlies the Gamlan Formation, is exposed. The mudstone locally contains thin lenses of pyrite and pyrrhotite with minor quantities of other sulphides. On the eastern side of the valley (Figure 42) there is an excellent small outcrop in an anticline in the basal Maentwrog Formation (see Excursion 3). Beds of fine quartzose sandstone up to 15 cm thick alternate with very dark silty mudstone. Some beds, probably turbidites, are massive, others display cross-lamination, rippled tops and convoluted lamination (see p. 24). The bases of the beds are load deformed with additional, later, tectonic deformation. Unlike the sandstone, the mudstone displays a strong cleavage.

The road along the Mawddach estuary, though it crosses

Figure 42 Basal Maentwrog Formation at Aber Amffra harbour

the Caerdeon syncline and skirts the end of the Dolwen pericline, remains within the Maentwrog Formation as far as Ganllwyd. There are numerous exposures, many of them stabilised with rock anchors, and all aspects of the formation may be examined.

Locality 6 [6793 1888]   Park in the lay-by where the road has been re-routed. In this southern part of the Harlech dome the upper part of the Maentwrog Formation contains very little interbedded sandstone and coarse quartzose siltstone. The outcrop is typical of the upper part of this formation. The dark grey banded silty mudstone is intruded by a 20-m thick sill of grey, altered, pyritic microtonalite, and the contact is exposed. The rock is typical of the numerous intrusions which are co-magmatic with the Rhobell Volcanic Group lavas. In the drift above the outcrop a channel, filled with rounded boulders and cobbles in a clayey matrix, occurs below the scree or head. There are several similar examples along this road (see *Locality 9*). They represent active subglacial drainage channels which were filled with alluvium, and which were eventually covered by scree following deglaciation.

Convolute lamina-
tion

Locality 7 [7011 1954]   About 40 m along a Forestry Commission road on the north side of the A496 is a bricked-up
entrance to a level in the Prince of Wales gold mine. There
are numerous levels on the hillside in this area all worked in
a group of E–W-trending quartz veins carrying galena,
pyrite and chalcopyrite. Voel Mine, near the top of Foel
Ispri, is included in the New Precipice Walk (Excursion 13).
The veins have been mined since the middle 18th century,
though work at the Prince of Wales mine began only in 1836.
Efforts to make them profitable continued until 1903. Very
little gold was found, and throughout their history lead, zinc
and silver were the main products.

About 30 m beyond the adit is a 4 to 5-m section through
boulder clay which shows a crude layering. There is a
dominance of rounded exotic cobbles in silty clay in the
lower part and locally derived angular boulders and cobbles
in the upper part. The boulder clay is overlain by about 1 m
of soliflucted debris with incorporated waste from mine
workings.

Locality 8 [7107 1937]   This relatively new road cutting
alongside a scree retaining wall is a good place to examine
the upper part of the Maentwrog Formation. The section exposes dark grey mudstone with silty laminae, laminae and
thin beds of coarse quartzose siltstone, and two beds, up to
26 cm thick, of fine quartzose sandstone showing convoluted
lamination in the upper parts. The mudstone is locally
pyritic with lenses, disseminated crystals and some 1 cm
cubes. The outcrop is crossed by a 50-cm thick fault-zone
with an easterly downthrow and several parallel fractures. A
strong N–S tectonic lineation is apparent on bedding surfaces, but no cleavage is visible in outcrop.

Locality 9 [7212 2047]   Near the north end of the long road
cutting north of Llanelltyd is another example of a filled
subglacial drainage channel. Here a winding channel eroded
into the Maentwrog Formation is filled with a mixture of
boulders, cobbles and sand, in places with a hard ferruginous
cement. The scree which covered the channel was stripped
off during road widening.

Locality 10 [7283 2445]   Just north of the Tyn-y-groes hotel
the Mawddach valley widens. From this point to the confluence of the Afon Eden, about 1.5 km N, it is filled with
terraced deposits of late or post-glacial sands and gravels, in
places with a hard ferruginous or manganiferous cement.
Details of this locality are given on p. 72.

The Maentwrog Formation, exposed in the river bed
here, contains many fossils but of few species. *Homagnostus
obesus* and *Olenus* species are the commonest forms and have
been found at many localities. One of the earliest to be

discovered was on the banks of the river 700 m N of the Tyn-y-groes hotel.

North of Ganllwyd, about 1.5 km beyond the forest [7135 3055], there is a splendid view of the Rhinogs. The axis of the Dolwen pericline lies along the valley floor to the west. Bedding along the Rhinogs dips generally west, whereas on Craig-y-Penmaen, the craggy hill to the east of this locality, bedding dips east.

Locality 11 [7068 3667]   On the east side of the road, opposite a lay-by, is a recently made cutting in the Rhinog Formation. The coarse-grained greywacke shows many of the features typical of turbidites (p. 15, Figure 9).

Locality 12 [6315 3940]   Park in a lay-by on the north side of the road. The Ffestiniog Flags Formation is well exposed, and consists of dark grey, cleaved mudstone thinly inter-bedded with coarse siltstone up to 15 cm thick dipping generally northwards. Most of the sedimentological characteristics of this formation (p. 28) can be examined here. At this locality crenulations and a strong tectonic lineation are imposed on the sedimentary structures.

References

ALLEN, P. M., COOPER, D. C., FUGE, R. and REA, W. J. 1976. Geochemistry and relationships to mineralisation of some igneous rocks from the Harlech Dome, Wales. *Trans. Inst. Min. Metall.*, Vol. 85, pp. B100–108.

— EASTERBROOK, G. D. 1978. Mineralised breccia pipe and other intrusion breccias in Harlech Dome, north Wales. *Trans. Inst. Min. Metall.*, Vol. 87, pp. B157–161.

— JACKSON, A. A. 1978. Bryn-teg Borehole, North Wales. *Bull. Geol. Surv. G.B.*, No. 61, 51 pp.

— — RUSHTON, A. W. A. 1981. The stratigraphy of the Mawddach Group in the Cambrian succession of North Wales. *Proc. Yorkshire Geol. Soc.*, Vol. 43, pp. 295–329.

ANDREW, A. R. 1910. The geology of the Dolgelly Gold Belt, North Wales. *Geol. Mag.*, Dec. 5, Vol. 7, pp. 159–171, 201–211, 261–271.

COX, A. H. and WELLS, A. K. 1927. The geology of the Dolgelly District, Merionethshire. *Proc. Geol. Assoc.*, Vol. 38, pp. 265–331.

CRIMES, T. P. 1970. A facies analysis of the Cambrian of Wales. *Palaeogeogr., Palaeoclimatol., Palaeoecol.*, Vol. 7, pp. 113–170.

DZULINSKI, S. and WALTON, E. K. 1965. Sedimentary features of flysch and greywacke. In *Developments in Sedimentology*, Vol. 7. (Amsterdam: Elsevier Press.)

FEARNSIDES, W. G. 1905. On the geology of Arenig Fawr and Moel Llyfnant. *Q. J. Geol. Soc. London*, Vol. 61, pp. 608–640.

FOSTER, H. D. 1968. The glaciation of the Harlech Dome. Unpublished PhD thesis, University of London.

GLASBY, G. P. 1974. A geochemical study of the manganese ore deposits of the Harlech Dome, North Wales. *J. Earth Sci.*, Vol. 8, pp. 445–450.

HALL, G. W. 1975. *The gold mines of Merioneth.* (Gloucester: Griffin Publications.)

KOKELAAR, B. P. 1979. Tremadoc to Llanvirn Volcanism on the southeast side of the Harlech dome (Rhobell Fawr), N. Wales. Pp. 591–596 *in* The Caledonides of the British Isles — reviewed. HARRIS, A. L., HOLLAND, C. H., LEAKE, B. E. (Editors). *Spec. Pub. Geol. Soc. London*, No. 8.

LYNAS, B. D. T. 1973. The Cambrian and Ordovician rocks of the Migneint area, North Wales. *J. Geol. Soc. London*, Vol. 129, pp. 481–503.

MATLEY, C. A. and WILSON, T. S. 1946. The Harlech Dome, north of the Barmouth estuary. *Q. J. Geol. Soc. London*, Vol. 102, pp. 1–40.

MOHR, P. A. 1964. Genesis of the Cambrian manganese rocks of North Wales. *J. Sediment. Petrol.*, Vol. 34, pp. 819–829.

MORRISON, T. A. 1975. *Goldmining in Western Merioneth.* (Llandysul: Merioneth Historical and Records Society.) 98 pp.

RAMSAY, A. C. 1866. The geology of North Wales. *Mem. Geol. Surv. G.B.*, Vol. 3, 381 pp.

Ricci-Lucci, F. 1975. Depositional cycles in turbidite formations. *J. Sediment. Petrol.*, Vol. 45, pp. 3–43.

Ridgway, J. 1975. The stratigraphy of Ordovician volcanic rocks on the southern and eastern flanks of the Harlech Dome in Merionethshire. *Geol. J.*, Vol. 10, pp. 87–106.

Rice, R. and Sharp, G. 1976. Copper mineralisation in the forest of Coed-y-Brenin, Wales. *Trans. Inst. Min. Metall.*, Vol. 85, pp. B1–13.

Rushton, A. W. A. 1982. The biostratigraphy and correlation of the Merioneth – Tremadoc Series boundary in North Wales. Pp. 41–59 *in* The Cambrian–Ordovician boundary: sections, fossil distributions, and correlations. Bassett, M. G. and Dean, W. T. (Editors). *National Museum of Wales, Geological Series*, No. 3.

Sedgwick, A. 1852. On the classification and nomenclature of the Lower Palaeozoic rocks of England and Wales. *Q. J. Geol. Soc. London*, Vol. 8, pp. 136–168.

Walker, R. G. 1965. The origin and significance of the internal sedimentary structure of turbidites. *Proc. Yorkshire Geol. Soc.*, Vol. 35, pp. 1–32.

Wells, A. K. 1925. The geology of the Rhobell Fawr district (Merioneth). *Q. J. Geol. Soc. London*, Vol. 81, pp. 463–538.

Woodland, A. W. 1939. The petrography and petrology of the Lower Cambrian manganese ore of west Merionethshire. *Q. J. Geol. Soc. London*, Vol. 95, pp. 1–35.

— (Editor.) 1971. The Llanbedr (Mochras Farm) Borehole. *Rep. Inst. Geol. Sci.*, No. 71/18, 115 pp.

Glossary

Acid-ic   Relating to igneous rocks containing over 63 per cent silica
Altiplanation terrace   Hillside bench cut in solid rock and formed in periglacial conditions by processes involving solifluction and mass movement
Argillaceous   Relating to sediment composed of clay sized particles
Autoclastic breccia   A rock formed by mechanical crushing *in situ*
Basalt   Fine-grained, dark coloured igneous rock, usually extrusive, composed mainly of plagioclase in the labradorite to bytownite range and pyroxene
Base metal   Common chemically active metal; for example, lead, copper, zinc
Basic   Relating to igneous rocks with less than 52 per cent of silica
Benthonic   Relating to bottom-dwelling marine life
Bornite   Sulphide of copper and iron (Cu_5FeS_4) with iridescent tarnish (Peacock Ore)
Boulder Clay   Glacial deposit consisting of unsorted boulders and pebbles in clay matrix. Synonymous with till
Brachiopod   Solitary marine invertebrate characterised by having two symmetrical but dissimilar shells or valves
Breccia   A coarse-grained clastic rock composed of angular rock fragments
Breccia pipe   Roughly cylindrical body of intrusive breccia
Caledonian orogeny   Name used for the orogenic belt (the Caledonides) stretching from Ireland through Britain to Scandinavia. Dated as end-Silurian but also used to include earlier pulses
Chalcopyrite   Bright brass-yellow ore mineral of copper ($CuFeS_2$)
Chronostratigraphy   Branch of stratigraphy which relates strata to time
Cleavage   Fissile structure in a rock produced by deformation or metamorphism which enables it to split into thin laminae along secondary aligned fractures
Comagmatic   Related to igneous rocks interpreted as having been derived from a common parent-magma

Contourite   Sedimentary rock deposited from a contour-following bottom current. Usually recognised as a layer of relatively coarse-grained sediment in marine muds or silts
Dolerite   Medium-grained, igneous intrusive rock of similar composition to basalt
Drumlin   Low, oval hill or ridge of glacial till built under the margin of the ice and shaped by its flow so that the longer axis is parallel with the direction of movement of the ice
Epiclastic   Related to a rock formed by the breakdown and consolidation of pre-existing rocks
Fluvioglacial   Related to the deposits produced by meltwater streams flowing from a glacier
Fold   Bend of a planar structure in rocks, for example, bedding planes or cleavage
Fold axis   Line on a map which traces the crest or trough of a fold
Galena   Bluish grey ore mineral of lead (PbS)
Geosyncline   Large-scale downwarp in the surface of the earth in which thousands of metres of sedimentary and volcanic rocks accumulate
Graptolites   Extinct group of colonial marine animals with a corneous skeleton. In *Dictyonema* the colony formed a conical net
Greenschist facies   Low grade regional metamorphism corresponding to a temperature range of 300 to 500°C
Greywacke   An impure sandstone with more than 15 per cent interstitial matrix consisting of mica, chlorite and quartz. Grains include quartz, feldspar and lithic rock fragments
Head   Deposit consisting of locally derived unsorted material formed by solifluction usually under periglacial conditions
Hiatus   Break in continuity of the stratigraphic record either by erosion or non-deposition, and the time-value associated with this period

Hyaloclastite   A deposit formed by the rapid chilling of a lava or magma where it flows into water or saturated sediment causing it to shatter into small angular fragments

Hydrothermal alteration   The alteration of rocks or minerals by the action of hot water circulating underground

Hyolithid   Extinct group of molluscs with a narrowly conical lidded shell

Intermediate   Relating to igneous rocks containing 52 to 63 per cent silica

Intrusive breccia   Heterogeneous mixture of angular fragments which has been mobilised and intruded into its present position

Lapilli   Fragments between 2 and 64 mm in diameter ejected by a volcanic eruption

Lava breccia   Autoclastic breccia produced by the fragmentation of the upper and lower crusts of a lava during flow

Lithostratigraphy   That part of stratigraphy which deals with the nature and composition of strata

Load cast   A sole mark or depression on the base of a bed caused by unequal settling and compaction of the overlying material

Magnetite   Ore mineral of iron (Fe_3O_4)

Mass-flow deposits (mud flow)   Deposit formed by mass-movement of soil and rock debris down a slope. May be triggered by earthquake or by oversaturation

Mass wasting   Dislodgement and downslope movement of soil and rock material under gravity. Includes processes such as solifluction, rock slides, soil creep and mass-flow

Microdiorite   Medium-grained intermediate igneous rock consisting of plagioclase in the oligoclase to andesine range. Other minerals may include augite, hornblende, biotite, hypersthene. Primary quartz is normally less than 5 per cent

Microgranite   Medium-grained acid igneous rock containing quartz and feldspar with some dark minerals which may include hornblende and biotite

Microtonalite   Medium-grained intermediate igneous rock of similar composition to microdiorite but containing more than 10 per cent primary quartz

Molybdenite   Lead-grey flaky molybdenum mineral (MoS_2)

Moraine   Debris eroded and redeposited by a glacier consisting of unsorted unstratified till. Lateral and terminal moraines are the deposits at the side and end of a glacier respectively

Oolith   Round or oval accretionary particle in a sedimentary rock (0.25 to 2 mm in diameter)

Orogeny   Process of formation of mountains

Pericline   A fold in the form of a dome or basin

Periglacial   Relating to the conditions and processes existing around the margins of a glacier or ice-sheet

Phenocryst   Large conspicuous crystal in a porphyritic rock

Porphyry   An igneous rock of any composition containing phenocrysts in a fine-grained groundmass

Porphyry copper   An ore deposit composed of a large body of rock containing small quantities of disseminated chalcopyrite and other sulphide mineral

Pyrite   Brass-yellow ore of iron known as 'fools gold' (FeS_2)

Pyrrhotite   Silver-yellow magnetic form of iron sulphide

Quartz-microdiorite   A form of microdiorite with between 5 and 10 per cent quartz

Quartz wacke   Impure sandstone containing more than 15 per cent detrital matrix (sericite and chlorite). Grains are mainly of quartz with less than 10 per cent feldspar and less than 10 per cent of rock fragments

Rhodochrosite   Pink or reddish ore of manganese ($MnCO_3$)

Solifluction   Downslope flow of waterlogged soil and other unsorted material

Spessartine   Red-brown to yellowish manganese aluminium silicate (variety of garnet)

Sphalerite   Yellowish brown to dark brown zinc ore (ZnS)

Subarkose   Sandstone with little detrital matrix (less than about 15 per cent) with grains predominantly of feldspar with less abundant lithic clasts and quartz

Subgreywacke   Sandstone with little detrital matrix (as in subarkose). Grains consist of quartz, rock fragments and feldspar. The proportion of rock fragments exceeds that of feldspar

Subduction   Process whereby one part of the earth's crust descends beneath another

Subvolcanic   Relating to intrusions and other phenomena in the basement beneath a volcano

Till   Synonymous with boulder clay

Trilobite   An extinct group of marine anthropods (class Trilobita) in which the exoskeleton was divided longitudinally into three lobes (Figure 20)

Tuff   A rock formed by the consolidation of volcanic ash

Tuffite   A mixed rock consisting of >25 per cent pyroclastic and >25 per cent epiclastic or detrital material

Turbidite   The consolidated deposit of a turbidity current. These rocks are characterised by graded bedding, moderate sorting and well developed sequence of bedding structures (Bouma cycle)

Xenolith   A foreign inclusion in an igneous rock

Index

Acerocare Zone 36
Acid tuff 43, 46
Allt Lŵyd Formation 4, 7, 38, 46, 81
Andesitic lava 4
Aran Fawddwy Formation 42
Aran Volcanic Group 2, 7, 8, 38, 46, 80
Ash-flow tuff 8, 42

Barmouth Formation 3, 6, 17, 52
Basalt 7, 29, 46, 80
Basic tuff 46, 47
Benglog Volcanic Formation 7, 41, 47
Breccia 9, 69, 71
Bioturbation 40
Boreholes
   Bryn-teg 4, 12
   Mochras 1, 63, 82
Bouma cycle 15, 17, 52
Boulder clay 48

Cleavage 12, 20, 58, 62, 65, 71, 84
Clogau Formation 6, 20, 66, 85
Columnar joints 46
Contourites 6, 24
Contact metamorphism 55
Cwmhesgen Formation 3, 33, 38, 44, 80

Devensian 9, 68
Dictyonema flabelliforme 21, 36, 46
Dol-cyn-afon Member 34, 36, 44
Dolgellau Member 3, 34, 42
Dolwen Formation 3, 11, 12
Dolerite 8, 31, 62
Drumlin 53

Erratic 55, 62

Faults
   Bala 8
   Mochras 2, 8
   Trawsfynydd 77
Ffestiniog Flags Formation 3, 28, 33, 43, 69, 88
Fluvioglacial sediments 47

Gamlan Formation 3, 6, 18, 52, 75, 79, 84
Garth Grit Member 36, 40, 46
Hafotty Formation 3, 6, 9, 13, 16, 53, 63
Harlech Grits Group 2, 3, 6, 12
Head 46, 53
Horse-whim 24
Hyaloclastite 8, 42

Iapetus 4
Intrusion complex 31
Landslip 38, 47
Lingulella davisii 28, 33
Llanbedr Formation 3, 12, 62, 82
Maentwrog Formation 3, 6, 20, 23
Manganese ore 6, 9, 15, 63, 84
Mawddach Group 2, 3
Melau Formation 8, 47
Mesozoic 63, 82
Microtonalite 8, 22, 25, 69, 74, 76, 86
Mines
   Bedd-y-coedwr 78
   Clogau 9, 18, 20, 22, 24, 66
   Cwm Hesian 77
   Dol-frwynog 25, 28
   Gwynfynydd 9, 72, 75, 77
   Haffotty 50, 53
   Panorama 55
   Prince of Wales 87
   Princess Marina 78
   St David's 22, 24
   Turf Copper 9, 25, 74
   Tyddyn Gwladys 74
   Vigra 18, 67
   Voel 69, 87
Moraine 62

Offrwm Volcanic Formation 46
Olenus Zone 72
Oolitic ironstone 40
Orusia lenticularis 34, 44

Parabolina spinulosa 34, 44
Paradoxides davidis 20
Phosphatic nodules 34, 36
Platysolenites antiquissimus 12
Porphyry copper 25, 71, 74, 77
Pillow lava 42
Rhinog Formation 3, 6, 53, 58
Rhobell Volcanic Group 2, 3, 4, 29
Scoria 47
Site of Special Scientific Interest 34
Slate 43, 62, 82
Solifluction 65, 72, 87
Sub-glacial channels 86
Tertiary 1, 2, 8, 82
Tuff 46, 52
Tuffite 36, 40, 46
Turbidites 5, 15, 24, 82

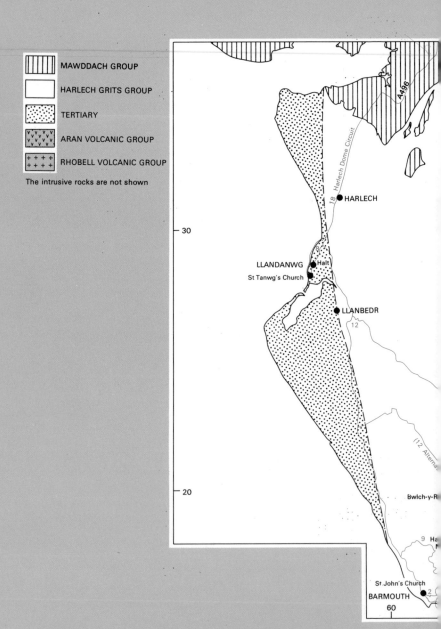

MAWDDACH GROUP

HARLECH GRITS GROUP

TERTIARY

ARAN VOLCANIC GROUP

RHOBELL VOLCANIC GROUP

The intrusive rocks are not shown

— 30

— 20

Harlech Dome Circuit

18 ● HARLECH

LLANDANWG ● Halt
St Tanwg's Church ●

● LLANBEDR

12

(12 Alterna

Bwlch-y-R

9 Ha

St John's Church
BARMOUTH ●
60